SCIENCE DICTIONARY

PETER ROBSON

Newby Books

PO BOX 40, SCARBOROUGH,
NORTH YORKSHIRE YO12 5TW
TEL/FAX 01723 362713
www.newbybooks.co.uk

SAFETY FIRST!

1) Laboratories often contain apparatus or substances which can be dangerous if used incorrectly. If in doubt, always ask.

   Dangerous substances include sodium, potassium, calcium, mercury, acids and crude oil - and there are many others.

2) Never taste chemicals or organisms unless your teacher suggests that you should.

3) It is very dangerous to look directly at the Sun, even through dark glasses or dark filters. It is even more dangerous to try looking at the Sun through binoculars or a telescope. Doing so would damage your eyes permanently or cause blindness. Think what happens to a piece of paper if you focus the Sun's rays on it with a magnifying glass (convex lens).

   For the same reason, you should not look directly at burning magnesium.

4) When doing chemical experiments, wear goggles. If you have to walk about, walk slowly and be aware of other people.

5) When heating substances in a test-tube or flask, always make sure that the open end of the tube or flask is pointing away from other people and yourself.

6) Hot glass takes a long time to cool down, so always leave it for several minutes before touching it.

7) If you leave a Bunsen burner alight, always close the air hole so that you and other people can see the flame.

8) Always wash your hands after working with chemicals or biological specimens (plants, animals, fungi, etc.).

SAFETY FIRST!

9) Mains electricity (240 volts) can kill. Never experiment with mains electricity or use it at all unless you are strictly supervised. Always switch off and unplug any mains equipment after use. Make sure your hands are dry before touching any electrical equipment, including switches and plugs.

10) Wear old or protective clothing (apron, overalls, etc.) when doing practical work, experiments, etc., especially in chemistry and biology.

11) (a) There are not many dangerous animals in the United Kingdom, but some animals will attack if they are cornered or startled.

(b) The only poisonous snake in the U.K. is the adder, which can normally be identified by its zigzag pattern (though occasionally adders do not have the pattern). Adders do not usually attack unless you annoy them or step on them.

(c) Many insects have unpleasant bites or stings.

(d) Some fungi are deadly poisonous, so always check, even if they look rather like mushrooms.

In this book, the words are listed in alphabetical order
ABCDEFGHIJKLMNOPQRSTUVWXYZ.

If a word is difficult to say, the pronunciation (how to say it) is put in brackets after the word. The stressed part of the word is underlined.

For example, **SAUSAGES** (pr. soss-ee-jiz) means that sausages is pronounced soss-ee-jiz with the stress on the first part of the word.

e.g. stands for Latin ‘exempli gratia’ which means ‘for example’.

i.e. stands for Latin ‘id est’ which means ‘that is’ or ‘in other words’.

etc. stands for Latin ‘et cetera’ which means ‘and so on’ or ‘and other things’.

$\bumpeq$ means ‘roughly equal to’.

ABDOMEN (1) The part of the body of a vertebrate which contains the liver, kidneys, stomach and intestines.

(2) The lowest, or furthest back, of the three main parts of an arthropod.

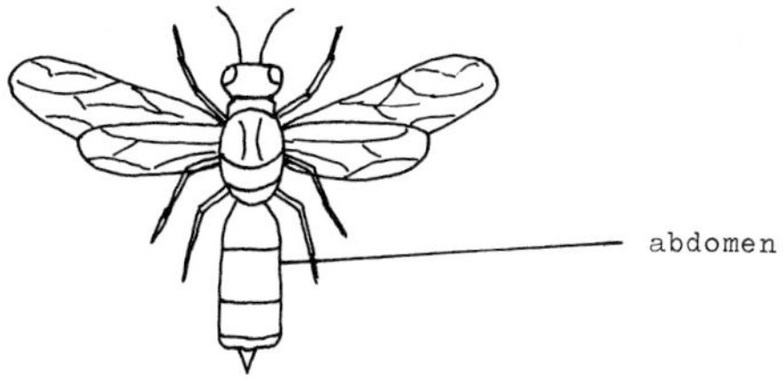

(Ruby-tailed wasp)

ABSOLUTE ZERO The lowest (calculated) possible temperature (–273°C). At absolute zero the atoms of a substance would remain completely still.

ACID A substance which has a pH of less than 7.

Acids include hydrochloric acid, nitric acid, sulphuric acid, lemon juice (citric acid), vinegar (acetic acid) and many others.

An acid can be neutralised by an alkali or base to form a salt and water.

Acidic oxides (oxides which form acids when they are dissolved in water) are non-metal oxides, e.g. carbon dioxide, sulphur dioxide.

ACID RAIN Rain containing acid substances such as sulphur dioxide and nitrogen oxides which have been given off in smoke or fumes from factories, car exhausts, etc., or produced by plankton in lakes and seas, and have dissolved in the water droplets in the air. Acid rain often kills trees and other plants, pollutes streams and rivers (killing fish and other aquatic life) and damages buildings made from limestone, etc.

AEROBIC RESPIRATION Respiration using oxygen. See RESPIRATION.

AIDS Acquired Immune Deficiency Syndrome. A serious, and often fatal (resulting in death) disease, caused by the HIV virus. See HIV.

AIR A mixture of gases surrounding the Earth. Air consists of nitrogen (about 78%), oxygen (about 21%), argon (nearly 1%) and small amounts of carbon dioxide, helium, neon, krypton, xenon, water vapour and other substances.

ALCOHOL A liquid compound containing carbon, hydrogen and oxygen, and often used as a solvent. There are many different kinds of alcohol.

The alcohol in alcoholic drinks (wine, beer, cider, whisky, etc.) is ethanol (ethyl alcohol) formed when the sugar in fruit, grain or vegetables ferments.

Methylated spirit is a mixture consisting mainly of ethanol.

ALGAE (pr. al-gee or al-jee) Plants, or plant-like organisms, without roots, stems or leaves (each one is an alga). Algae obtain their energy by photosynthesis and usually live in water.

Examples. Seaweed.
The green scum (spirogyra) which forms on stagnant ponds.

ALKALI A solution of a base. An alkali is a substance which has a pH of more than 7.

Alkalis include caustic soda solution (sodium hydroxide), lime water (calcium hydroxide), ammonia (ammonium hydroxide) and others.

An alkali can be neutralised by an acid to form a salt and water.

Alkaline oxides (oxides which form alkalis when they are dissolved in water) are metal oxides, e.g. calcium oxide.

ALLOY Two or more metals (and sometimes also including non-metals) forming a single substance.

Examples. Brass (copper and zinc).
Bronze (copper and tin).
Stainless steel (iron, chromium and carbon).

ALUMINIUM An element. A silvery-white light metal, usually extracted from an ore called bauxite (aluminium oxide). Aluminium is used for making kitchen equipment (pans, etc.), aircraft parts (because it is light and does not corrode much), drinks cans and many other things.

The symbol for aluminium is Al.

AMMETER An instrument which measures electric current. The unit of current is an ampere (amp).

Circuit diagram symbol 

AMPERE The normal unit of electric current. Usually shortened to amp. Named after the French scientist André Marie Ampère (born 1775, died 1836).

AMPHIBIAN One of the class of cold-blooded, smooth-skinned vertebrates which, during part or all of their lives, can move and breathe both on land and under water.

Examples. Frog, toad, newt.

AMPLITUDE The distance from the centre to the outside of a wave. The amount of energy in a sound wave depends on its amplitude.

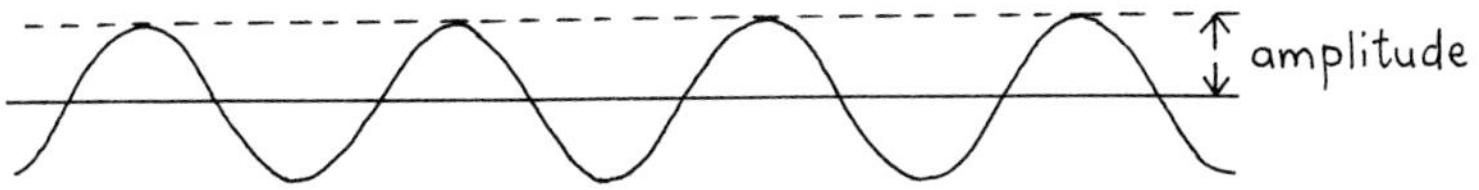

ANAEROBIC RESPIRATION Respiration without oxygen. See RESPIRATION.

AND CIRCUIT A logic circuit in which the output is high only when all the inputs are high.

Simplified circuit symbol 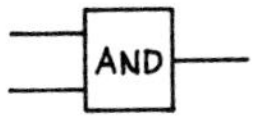

The truth table for an AND circuit with two inputs is

INPUTS		OUTPUT
0	0	0
0	1	0
1	0	0
1	1	1

ANEMOMETER An instrument for measuring wind speed.

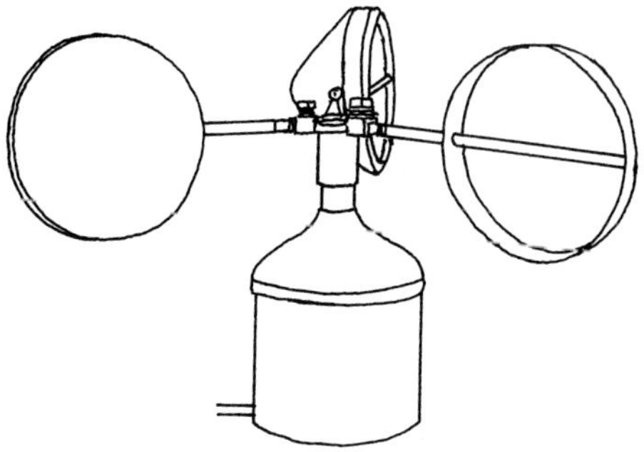

Cup anemometer

ANHYDROUS Without water. An anhydrous salt is a salt without water of crystallisation.

Example. Anhydrous (white) copper sulphate which turns to hydrated (blue) copper sulphate when water is added to it.

ANIMAL An organism which normally (a) has cells without cell walls; (b) can move of its own accord; (c) has sense organs such as eyes, nose, mouth, antennae, etc; (d) feeds on plants or other animals.

ANTHER The part of a stamen (at its tip) which produces pollen.

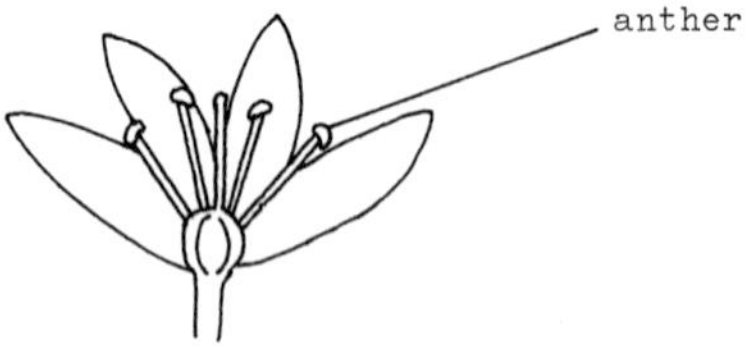

(Wood garlic)

ANTIBIOTIC A chemical (or drug) used for killing harmful bacteria and helping to cure certain illnesses. The best-known antibiotic is penicillin.

ANUS (pr. ay-nus) The opening at the end of the intestines through which faeces leave the body.

AQUATIC (pr. ak-wat-ik or ak-wot-ik) Living or growing in water.

Example. A dolphin is an aquatic mammal.

ARACHNID (pr. a-rak-nid) One of a class of arthropods including spiders, mites and scorpions. An arachnid has eight legs.

Spider

ARTERY One of the large blood vessels (tubes) carrying blood from the heart.

ARTHROPOD One of a group (or phylum) of invertebrates with jointed limbs, a segmented body and an exoskeleton.

Examples. Insects, arachnids, myriapods, crustaceans.

ASEXUAL (pr. ay-sex-yoo-al) Asexual reproduction is reproduction needing only one parent. The offspring (the newly-produced organisms) are genetically identical to the parent, i.e. they have exactly the same features as the parent.

Examples. Binary fission (cells), making spores (fungi), budding (plants).

ASTRONOMY The science which deals with heavenly bodies (objects in space) such as galaxies, stars, planets, satellites, etc.

ATMOSPHERE (pr. at-muss-fear) The envelope of gases surrounding a heavenly body (object in space). The Earth's atmosphere consists of air.

ATOM The smallest amount of an element which can take part in a chemical reaction.

An atom has a nucleus in the centre, and electrons moving about in the space surrounding the nucleus.

The simplest atom is an atom of hydrogen.

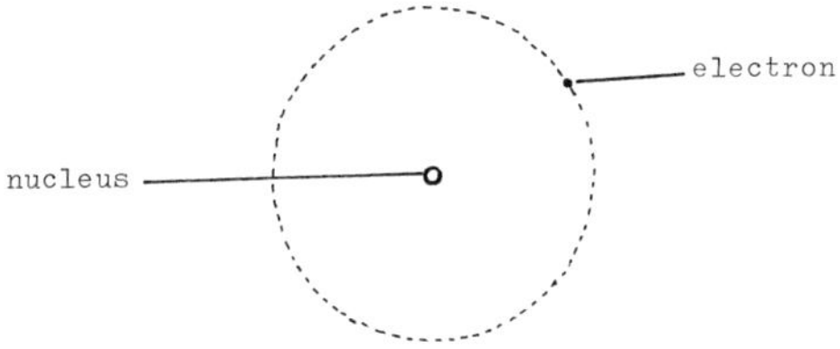

Hydrogen atom (not drawn to scale)

A row of about 30 000 000 (3×10^7) atoms side by side would fit between dots A and B.

A B

BACTERIA Tiny microscopic organisms (each one is a bacterium) which are important because they are decomposers, acting on rotting animal and plant life, including sewage, and forming useful chemicals. Some bacteria help to replace nitrates in the soil by absorbing nitrogen from the air. There are also some harmful bacteria which can cause disease, such as the bacteria which cause tuberculosis, cholera, etc.

BAROMETER An instrument for measuring air pressure. The scale of a barometer is usually marked in millibars (mb), millimetres (mm) or inches (in).

1000 mb = 750 mm = 29.5 in (approximately)

A barograph is a barometer which draws a graph of the air pressure over a certain period of time.

BASE A substance which neutralises an acid to form a salt and water.

Examples. Calcium oxide, copper oxide, magnesium oxide, sodium hydroxide.

A soluble base is an alkali and has a pH of more than 7.

BATTERY Two or more electrical cells grouped together, usually connected in series.

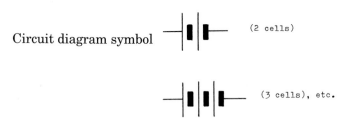

Circuit diagram symbol

(2 cells)

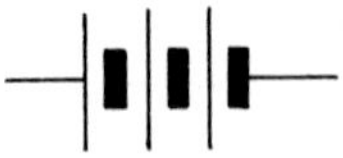

(3 cells), etc.

BEAKER A container used mainly for holding and pouring liquids.

Usually drawn

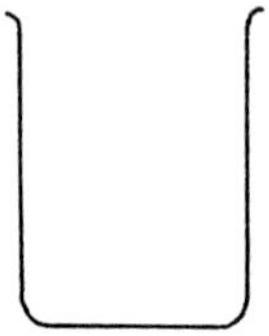

BINARY FISSION Asexual reproduction in which a cell splits into two similar cells.

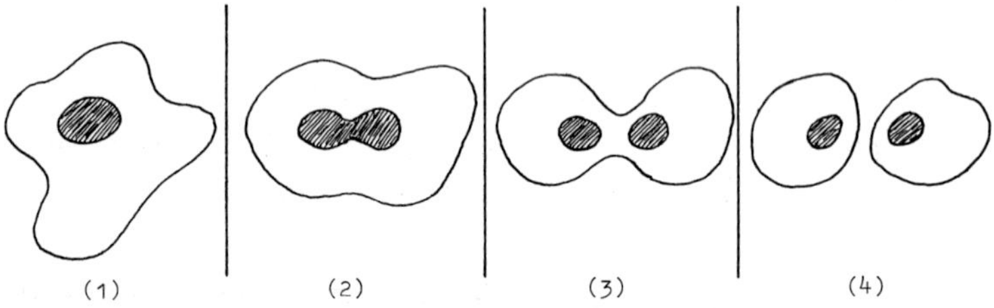

BINOCULARS (pr. bin-ok-yoo-luz) A device consisting of two telescopes side by side, used for viewing distant objects with both eyes at once. Like a telescope, binoculars magnify the objects, thus making them appear nearer.

BIODEGRADABLE A biodegradable substance is a substance which will decompose naturally through the action of decay organisms (decomposers).

BIOLOGY The study of living things. The branch of science which deals with plants, animals, fungi and other organisms.

BIOMASS The total mass of the living organisms in a certain area.

BIRD A warm-blooded vertebrate which normally (a) has wings; (b) has a body covered by feathers; (c) lays eggs.

BLADDER The sac in which urine from the kidneys is contained before leaving the body through the urethra. See KIDNEYS.

BLOOD The red liquid pumped round the body by the heart. Blood consists of

(a) plasma - a yellow liquid which contains dissolved proteins, glucose, urea, etc;

(b) red cells - which contain red haemoglobin, and carry oxygen;

(c) white cells (which are actually colourless, not white) - which help to protect the body against infection;

(d) platelets - fragments of cells which harden the blood to stop wounds bleeding.

BLOOD VESSEL A tube carrying blood round the body. The largest blood vessels are arteries and veins, and the smallest are capillaries.

BOIL A liquid boils (becomes a gas) when it becomes so hot that evaporation occurs not just at the surface but throughout the liquid. The bubbles of gas formed rise to the surface of the liquid.

BOILING POINT The temperature at which a liquid boils.
Example. The boiling point of water is 100°C. This is the temperature at which water (liquid) boils and becomes steam (gas).

BOURDON GAUGE An instrument for measuring air or gas pressure. It is made of a curled tube which uncurls when filled with compressed gas. The tube turns a pointer. Named after the French engineer Eugène Bourdon (born 1808, died 1884).

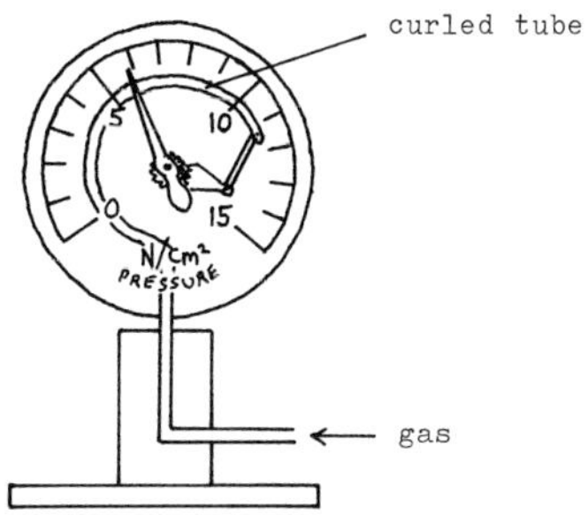

BRAIN The organ in the head of a vertebrate which controls and coordinates the movements and reactions of the body, and in which thinking and remembering take place.

BRASS An alloy of copper and zinc.

BRONZE An alloy of copper and tin.

BUD An early stage in the growth of leaves, flowers or branches. A bud consists of a short stem surrounded by closely-packed young leaves or petals.

BULB The round-shaped reproductive organ of certain plants such as tulips, daffodils, onions, etc. A bulb contains the future flower bud, leaves and stalk, surrounded by a thick covering of leaves.

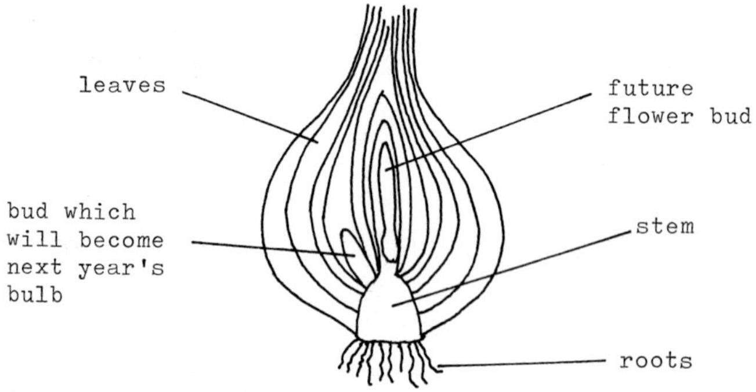

BUNSEN BURNER A gas burner whose flame can be made hotter or less hot by opening or closing an air hole. Named after the German scientist Robert W. Bunsen (born 1811, died 1899).

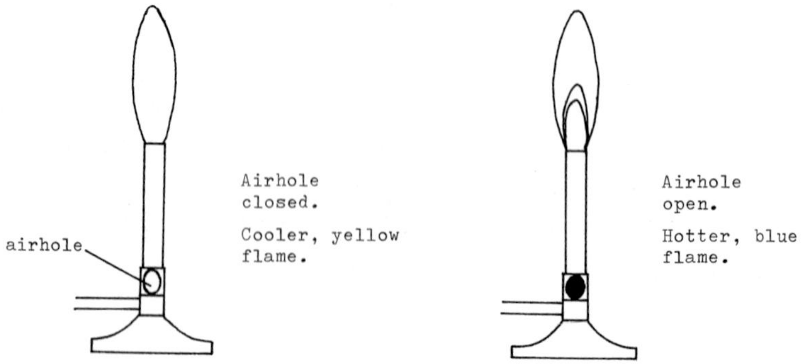

BURN When a substance burns, it combines with oxygen, giving off thermal (heat) energy and light energy.

BUZZER An electrical component which makes a buzzing sound when a current is passed through it.

Circuit diagram symbol 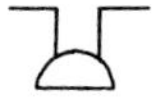

CALCIUM An element. A hard, silvery-white reactive metal.

( DANGEROUS SUBSTANCE. DO NOT EXPERIMENT WITH CALCIUM.)

Its compounds include, among many others, calcium oxide (quicklime), calcium hydroxide (slaked lime which dissolves to make lime water), calcium carbonate (chalk, limestone and marble) and calcium sulphate (gypsum, plaster of Paris and blackboard chalk).

Calcium compounds are an essential part of the human diet as they help to strengthen bones and teeth. Milk, cheese and yogurt contain calcium compounds.

The symbol for calcium is Ca.

CAPILLARY One of the thousands of tiny blood vessels forming networks throughout the body.

CAPILLARY TUBE A tube with a very fine bore. A very thin tube.

CARBOHYDRATE An energy-rich compound consisting of carbon, hydrogen and oxygen (with twice as many hydrogen atoms as oxygen atoms). Carbohydrates include starch, cellulose and sugars.

CARBON An element. A non-metal which is found in the earth as coal (an impure form of carbon), graphite and diamond. Many of its thousands of compounds are found in nature and are called organic compounds.

Graphite, the form of carbon used as 'lead' in ordinary pencils, is unusual because, although it is a non-metal, it is a good conductor of electricity.

The symbol for carbon is C.

CARBONATE A compound of carbon, oxygen and one or more other elements. A salt of carbonic acid. Carbonates include calcium carbonate (limestone, chalk, marble, etc.), sodium hydrogen carbonate (bicarbonate of soda) and many others.

When carbonates react with acids, carbon dioxide is released, e.g.

sodium carbonate + sulphuric acid → sodium sulphate + carbon dioxide ↑ + water

CARBON DIOXIDE A compound of carbon and oxygen. A colourless, slightly acidic, non-poisonous gas which is denser than air.

Carbon dioxide is produced by animals during respiration and from organic compounds in animals, plants and fungi when they rot or burn. Plants absorb carbon dioxide from the air during photosynthesis.

Carbon dioxide is used in certain kinds of fire extinguisher, as it does not support combustion (things cannot burn in it) and is frozen to make dry ice for refrigerating food. The bubbles in fizzy drinks are usually carbon dioxide.

Carbon dioxide can be tested by bubbling it through lime water which it turns milky-white.

The formula for carbon dioxide is CO_2.

CARBON MONOXIDE A compound of carbon and oxygen. A colourless poisonous gas formed when carbon burns incompletely (i.e. without enough oxygen for it to form carbon dioxide).

Carbon monoxide is one of the gases in car exhaust fumes, so it is dangerous to run a car engine in a closed garage. A blue flame in a coal fire is usually carbon monoxide burning.

The formula for carbon monoxide is CO.

CARNIVORE An animal (or, very rarely, a plant) which eats mainly animals.

Example. Sparrow-hawk.

A top carnivore is the animal which is at the end of a food chain and which is not eaten by any other animal.

CATALYST A chemical which speeds up the reaction of other chemicals but remains unchanged at the end of the reaction.

Examples. Enzymes are catalysts which speed up chemical reactions in the cells of organisms.
Manganese dioxide is a catalyst which speeds up the decomposition of hydrogen peroxide into oxygen and water.

CELL (1) The basic unit from which all organisms are made. Cells are the 'building blocks' of the living world, and consist of protoplasm (proteins and water). Every organism is made from at least one cell, but most are made from millions of different cells.

Examples. Animal cell (simplified)

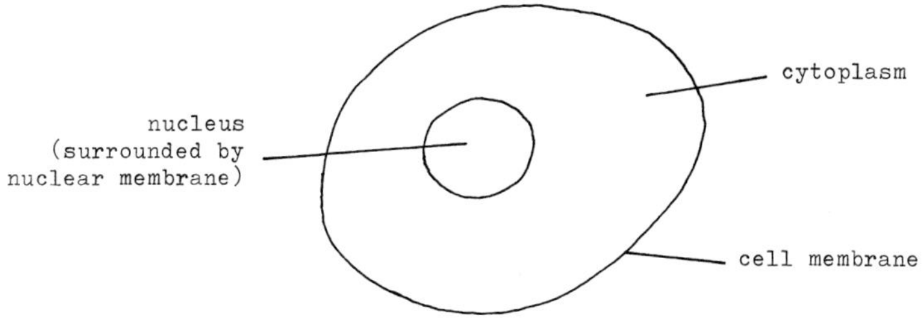

Plant cell of a green plant (simplified)

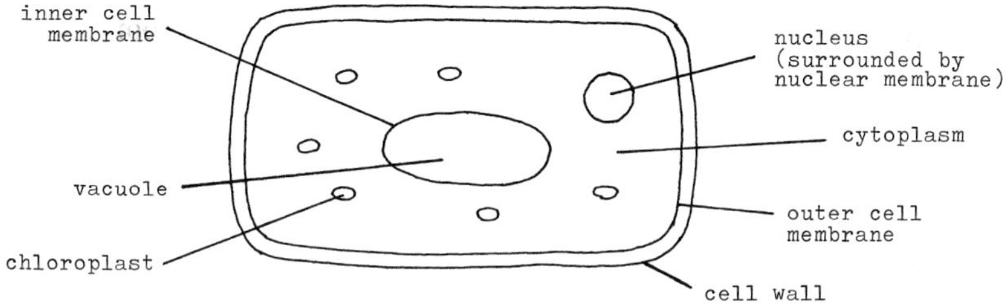

MOST cells contain cell membrane, cytoplasm and nucleus.

PLANT cells also contain a cellulose cell wall (the 'skeleton' of the plant), chloroplasts (where photosynthesis takes place) and a vacuole (containing cell sap which consists of water, sugar and mineral salts).

(2) A device which converts chemical energy (from a chemical reaction) into electrical energy to produce a current.

Circuit diagram symbol 

Example. 'Dry' cell (ordinary torch cell).

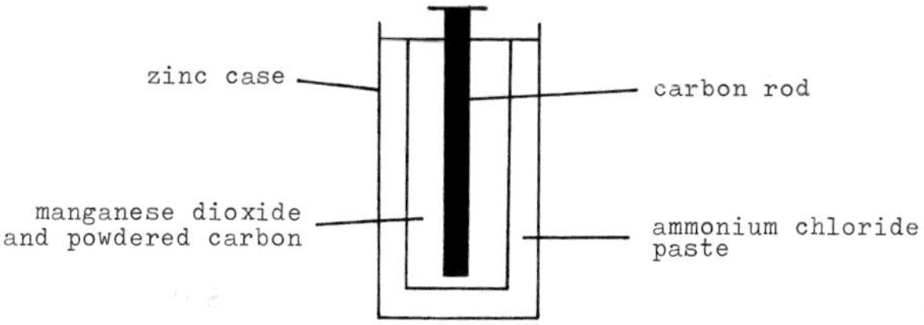

Two or more cells connected together, usually in series, make a battery.

CELLULOSE A kind of carbohydrate which forms the walls of plant cells. As part of the human diet, cellulose (fibre or roughage) is mostly undigested but exercises the muscles of the intestines.

Cellulose is the main substance in paper and film.

CELSIUS SCALE (pr. sell-see-us) A scale of temperatures with freezing point of water 0 degrees (0°C) and boiling point of water 100 degrees (100°C). Also called centigrade. Invented by the Swedish astronomer Anders Celsius (born 1701, died 1744).

CENTIGRADE SCALE Another name for Celsius scale.

CENTRIFUGAL FORCE (pr. sen-trif-yoo-gl or sen-tree-fyoo-gl) A force which acts outwards when an object is rotated.

Examples. A spin drier, in which centrifugal force separates the water from the clothes.

The centrifugal force acting on the Earth as it spins round, causing it to bulge at the Equator.

CHARGE The amount of electricity in an object or piece of material. A charge is either positive or negative. Objects with unlike charges (one positive, one negative) attract each other; objects with like charges (either both positive or both negative) repel each other. Charged objects also attract neutral objects.

CHEMICAL ENERGY The energy stored in atoms and molecules, and released during a chemical reaction.

Example. When hydrogen burns in air it combines with oxygen and releases energy.

hydrogen + oxygen → water (+ energy)

CHEMICAL REACTION A process in which atoms or molecules of substances, when the substances are put together, produce atoms or molecules of different substances.

Examples. iron + sulphur $\xrightarrow{\text{heat}}$ iron sulphide
zinc + hydrochloric acid → zinc chloride + hydrogen

CHEMISTRY The science which deals with the composition of matter, or what things are made of.

CHLORINE (pr. klaw-reen) An element. A yellowy-green poisonous gas (non-metal). One of the elements in hydrochloric acid, chlorides (e.g. common salt), etc.

It is used in the purification of water to destroy harmful bacteria.

The symbol for chlorine is Cl.

CHLOROPHYLL (pr. klaw-ro-fill) The green substance in a chloroplast which absorbs the light needed for photosynthesis.

Chlorophyll is a compound of carbon, hydrogen, oxygen, nitrogen and magnesium.

CHLOROPLAST One of the green parts of the cytoplasm in a plant cell. Chloroplasts contain chlorophyll. Photosynthesis takes place in the chloroplasts.

CHROMATOGRAPHY A method of separating soluble solids of different colours from a mixture of solids which have been dissolved in a solvent (such as water or ethanol).

Example. Spreading out a blob of black ink with water on blotting paper to produce rings of different-coloured dyes (a chromatogram).

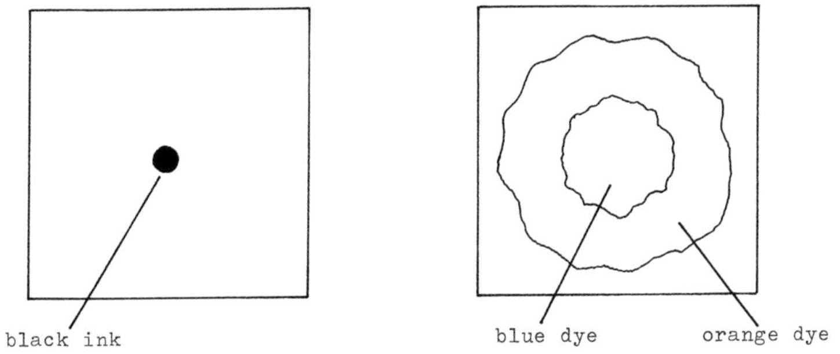

CHROMIUM An element. A silvery-white metal used for chromium plating and for making stainless steel.

The symbol for chromium is Cr.

CHROMOSOME A thread-like structure inside a cell nucleus, made mainly from a molecule of DNA, which duplicates itself when the cell divides.

Each chromosome is made up of thousands of genes (pr. jeenz), each of which carries the information (or chemical 'code') for passing on a certain feature (e.g. fair hair, brown eyes, etc.) to the next generation.

Normal human cells contain 46 chromosomes each (in 23 pairs), 23 from the father and 23 from the mother.

CHRYSALIS (pr. <u>kriss</u>-a-liss) The pupa of a butterfly or moth. The stage in the life of a butterfly or moth between a caterpillar (larva) and a fully-developed insect.

CIRCUIT (pr. <u>ser</u>-kit) The complete journey of an electric current. The path through which an electric current will flow.

CIRCUIT DIAGRAM A drawing showing a circuit, using symbols to represent components, and lines to represent connections.

Example.

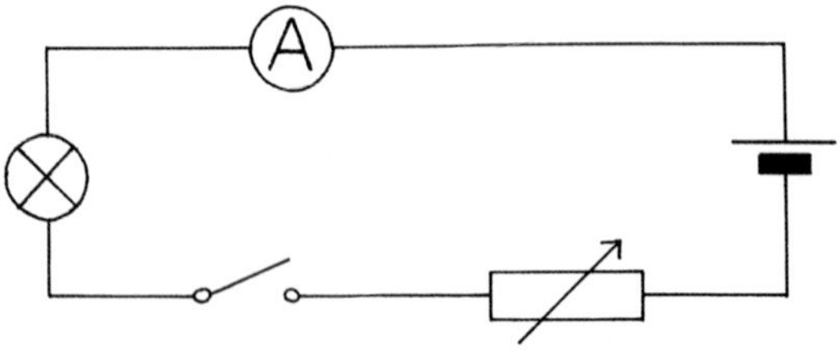

CIRCUIT SYMBOLS Drawings to represent components in a circuit diagram.

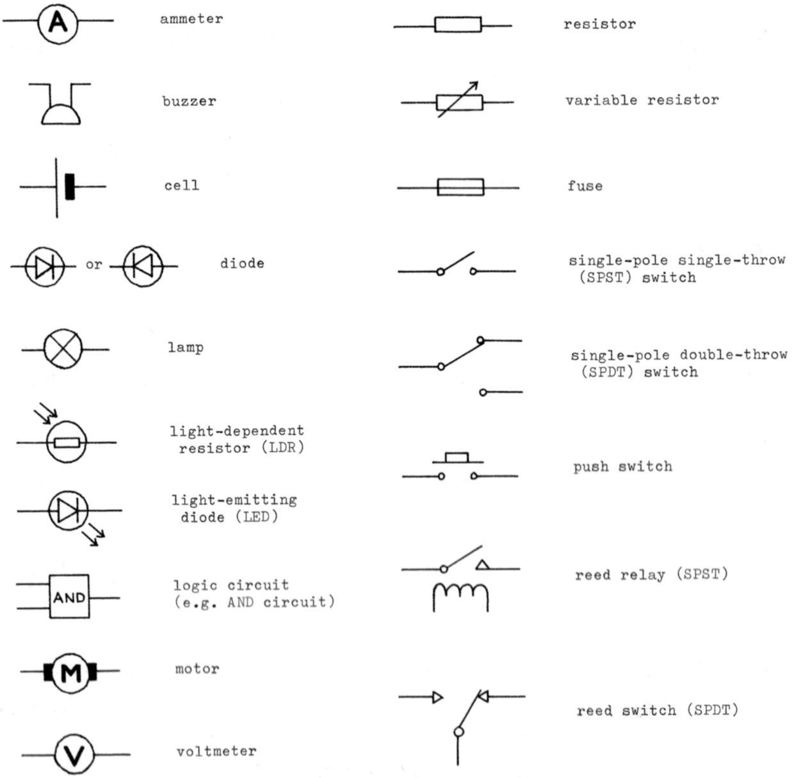

CIRCULATION The movement of blood round the body. The blood is pumped from the heart through arteries and returns to the heart through veins.

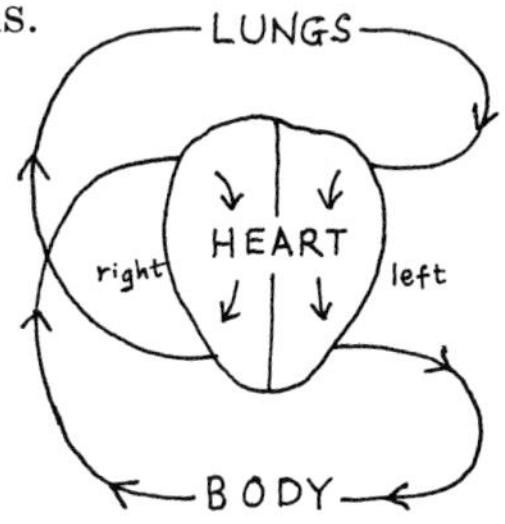

Diagram of human circulation (seen from the front)

Oxygen-enriched blood flows from the lungs to the left-hand side of the heart from where it is pumped throughout the body. The 'used' (deoxygenated) blood returns to the right-hand side of the heart from where it is pumped to the lungs to receive more oxygen.

CLASS A division of a phylum. See CLASSIFICATION

CLASSIFICATION The sorting out of organisms (living things) into groups with similar organisms in each group. The most basic groups are Kingdoms (which include Plants, Animals, etc.). Each kingdom is divided into further groups, each of which is called a Phylum. A phylum is divided into smaller groups called Classes, etc.

The names of the groups (from the most basic group down to each individual kind of organism) are KINGDOM / PHYLUM / CLASS /ORDER/ FAMILY / GENUS / SPECIES.

Example. <u>A yellow hammer</u> (species) is a kind of <u>bunting</u> (genus) which is a kind of <u>finch</u> (family) which is a kind of <u>perching bird</u> (order) which is a kind of <u>bird</u> (class) which is a kind of <u>chordate</u> (phylum) which is a kind of <u>animal</u> (kingdom).

The order of group names can be remembered by <u>K</u>ing <u>P</u>hillip <u>C</u>hoked <u>O</u>n <u>F</u>our <u>G</u>ob-<u>S</u>toppers

COAL A solid black or brown substance consisting of carbon and carbon compounds formed from plant life which has decomposed over millions of years. Coal is a fossil fuel.

COLD-BLOODED A cold-blooded animal has a body temperature which changes according to the outside temperature. All animals apart from birds and mammals are cold-blooded.

Cold-blooded animals cannot turn food into thermal energy (heat) and therefore become less active in cold weather.

COMBUSTION Burning. A chemical reaction in which a substance combines with oxygen, releasing thermal (heat) energy and light energy.

COMMON SALT Another name for sodium chloride.

COMMUNITY A group of populations of various different organisms all living in the same habitat.

COMPASS An instrument for finding direction. It usually consists of a magnet (magnetised steel needle) which can revolve on a pivot. The earth's magnetic field affects the magnet so that the north-seeking pole (north pole) points to magnetic north.

A plotting compass is a small compass used to show the magnetic field of a magnet.

COMPONENT A device, or piece of apparatus, used in an electrical circuit.

COMPOUND A substance consisting of two or more elements combined chemically. A compound cannot be separated into its elements except by a chemical reaction.

Examples. Water, sugar, copper sulphate.

Normally, a compound looks very different from the elements it contains, e.g. sugar is a white crystalline solid, quite different from carbon (usually a black solid), hydrogen (colourless gas) and oxygen (colourless gas) from which it is made.

CONCAVE A concave lens or concave mirror is one which curves inwards. See LENS and MIRROR.

CONCEIVE (pr. kon-seev) An animal is conceived (begun) when an egg is fertilised by a sperm. This process is called conception.

CONCENTRATED A concentrated solution is one in which a large amount of solute is dissolved in a small amount of solvent.

Concentrated acids are acids which are not much diluted (do not contain much water), e.g. concentrated sulphuric acid.

(☠ DANGER. DO NOT EXPERIMENT WITH CONCENTRATED ACIDS WITHOUT SUPERVISION.)

CONDENSATION The change of state of a substance from a gas to a liquid, normally caused by cooling (reducing the temperature).

Example. The condensation of steam to form water.

CONDUCTION Transfer of electricity or thermal (heat) energy through a substance by energy changes in the atoms, molecules or electrons of the substance.

CONDUCTOR A substance, or a device made of a substance, which allows electricity or thermal (heat) energy to pass through it easily.

Example. Copper is a good conductor of electricity and thermal energy.

CONE The scaly female flower of a coniferous tree. A cone has no ovary but contains ovules which are fertilised by pollen from the male flowers to form seeds. When the seeds are ripe, the scales of the cone, which have stayed shut to protect the seeds, open and let the seeds drift away.

(Japanese larch)

CONIFEROUS (pr. kon-iff-er-us) Coniferous trees are trees which have cones. Many coniferous trees (e.g. pine, spruce) are also evergreen but some are deciduous (e.g. larch). Coniferous trees usually have narrow, needle-like leaves.

CONSERVATION Keeping the natural world (or the environment) the same, or improving it, by preserving it and protecting it from destructive influences such as pollution, too many buildings, etc.

CONSERVATION OF ENERGY The law of conservation of energy states that (except in nuclear reactions) energy cannot be created or destroyed. In any system (such as an experiment or reaction) the sort of energy can change - for example, electrical energy can become light energy - but the total amount of energy stays the same.

CONSTELLATION A group of stars which appear in roughly the same part of the night sky, and form a distinct pattern.

Example. Orion

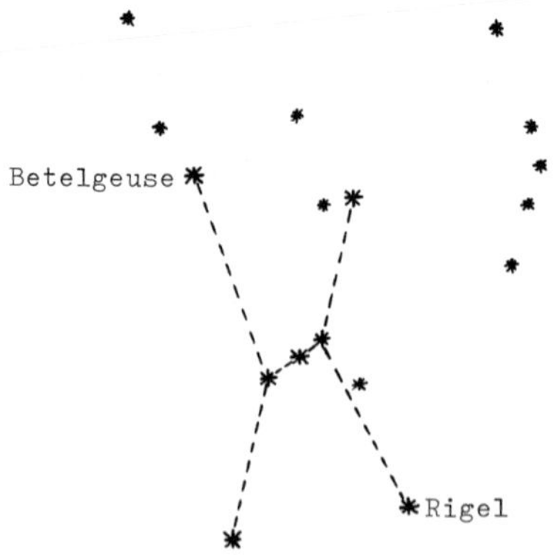

CONSUMER An organism (usually an animal) which eats producers or other consumers.

Primary consumer is a consumer which eats plant life. A herbivore.

Secondary consumer eats a primary consumer.

Tertiary consumer eats a secondary consumer.

CONTRACEPTION Preventing the fertilisation of an egg by a sperm. A contraceptive is a device or chemical (hormone) used to prevent fertilisation and therefore to limit the number of children conceived (birth control or family planning).

CONTRACT (pr. kon-<u>trakt</u>) Become smaller. Many substances contract when their temperature falls. A muscle contracts when its fibres are pulled together.

CONVEX A convex lens or convex mirror is one which curves outwards. See LENS and MIRROR.

COPPER An element. A reddy-orange metal which becomes tarnished with a bluey-green compound when it is left in air. Copper compounds are often green (e.g. copper carbonate) or blue (e.g. copper sulphate) and when heated in a flame they turn the flame green.

Copper is a very good conductor of thermal (heat) energy and electricity, and is used for making electrical cables and wires. It is also used to make brass (an alloy of copper and zinc), bronze (an alloy of copper and tin) and coins (an alloy of copper and zinc and/or nickel).

The symbol for copper is Cu (from its old name cuprum).

COPPER SULPHATE A compound of copper, sulphur and oxygen.
Anhydrous copper sulphate is a white powder; hydrated copper sulphate is blue crystals.
Anhydrous (white) copper sulphate can be used as a test for the presence of water, as it will turn blue even if only a small amount of water is present.

CORROSION A chemical reaction which eats or rots away a substance (usually a metal), producing another substance.
Example. Rusting. When iron is in contact with both air and water, corrosion takes place (the iron is corroded) to form rust (a kind of iron oxide).

CRUCIBLE A small bowl-shaped container, sometimes with a lid, used for heating solids to high temperatures.

Usually drawn  or 

CRUDE OIL Oil just as it comes out of an oil well, before going to a refinery. Many products, such as petrol, diesel fuel, plastics, paints, etc., are made from crude oil by fractional distillation.

(☠ DANGEROUS SUBSTANCE. DO NOT EXPERIMENT WITH CRUDE OIL.)

CRUSTACEAN (pr. krus-tay-shn) One of a class of arthropods, including crabs, lobsters, prawns, woodlice and others. Many crustaceans have a hard exoskeleton.

Example. Woodlouse.

CRYSTAL A piece of a solid which has formed with a definite structure or shape. Each crystalline substance forms crystals of its own special shape.

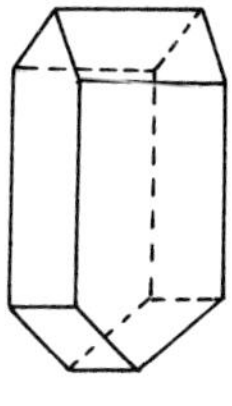

Crystal of Epsom salt
(magnesium sulphate)

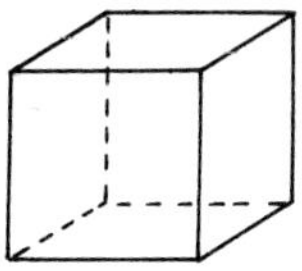

Crystal of common salt
(sodium chloride)

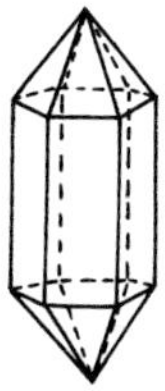

Crystal of quartz
(silicon dioxide)

(Simplified shapes)

CRYSTALLISATION Forming crystals, usually from a solution or from a molten (melted) substance.

CURRENT The flow of electricity, in the form of electrons, through a conductor. The rate of flow, also called the current, is measured in amperes (amps).

CUTTING A part, such as a stalk or leaf, cut from a plant, which makes roots to form a new plant.

CYTOPLASM (pr. sy-to-plazm) All the living parts of a cell, except for the nucleus.

Example.

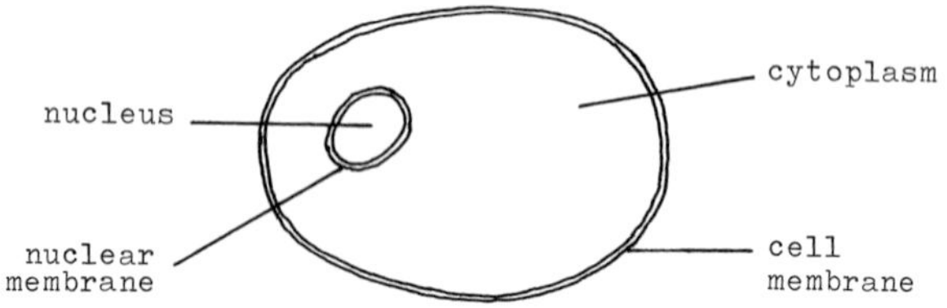

DECAY Rotting or decomposition of organic substances by fungi, bacteria or chemicals to make simpler substances. A decay organism (fungus, bacterium, etc.) is also called a decomposer.

DECIDUOUS (pr. diss-id-yoo-us) A deciduous plant is one which sheds all its leaves once a year.

Example. A sycamore is a deciduous tree.

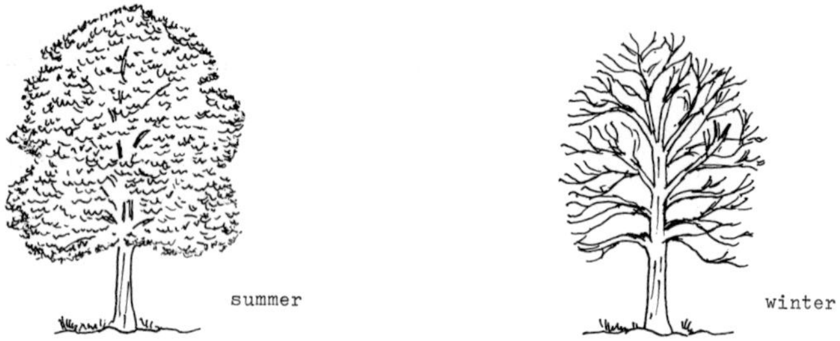

DECOMPOSER An organism, such as a fungus or bacterium, which breaks down (decomposes) dead tissue (plants, animals, etc.) into simpler chemicals.

DECOMPOSITION (1) The rotting of plant or animal matter by the action of bacteria, fungi or chemicals. Decomposition breaks down the organic chemicals and makes simpler substances.

(2) The splitting up of a compound into simpler substances.

Example. Copper carbonate $\rightarrow$ copper oxide + carbon dioxide

DEHYDRATED With the water removed. An animal or plant becomes dehydrated if it does not take in enough water. A chemical is dehydrated when it loses its water of crystallisation and becomes anhydrous.

DENSITY Mass per unit volume. The quantity found by dividing the mass (usually in grams) of an object or substance by its volume (usually in cubic centimetres). The unit of density is g/cm^3

$$\text{Density} = \frac{\text{Mass}}{\text{Volume}}$$

The density of pure water is $1g/cm^3$. Any substance denser than water will sink in water; any substance less dense will float. The density of a human being is close to $1g/cm^3$ as we are able to float on water as long as our lungs are full of air.

Some densities (in g/cm^3)

Air	0.0013	Ice	0.92
Aluminium	2.7	Iron	7.9
Balsa wood	0.2	Magnesium	1.7
Bone	1.9	Platinum	21.5
Charcoal	0.4	Silver	10.5
Copper	8.9	Stainless steel	7.8
Cork	0.25	Sulphur	2.1
Glass	2.5	Water	1.0
Gold	19.3		

DIAPHRAGM (pr. dy-a-fram) The muscular partition between the thorax and abdomen of a mammal.

Example. Diaphragm of a human being. The diaphragm contracts (goes down and flattens) when air is breathed into the lungs. It relaxes (goes up) when air is breathed out.

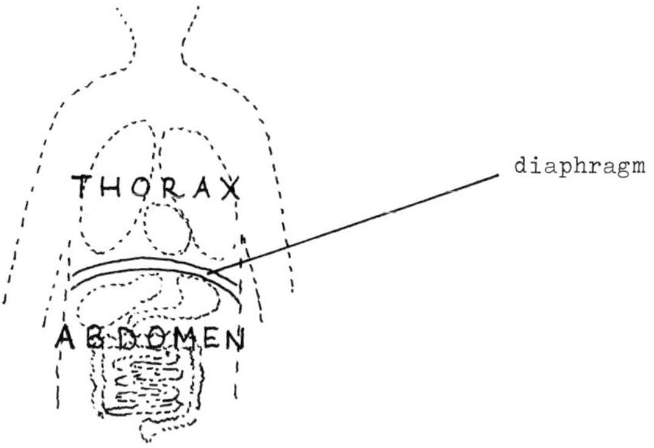

DIET The things which an animal normally eats or drinks. Some human beings go on a special diet because they are ill or wish to become slimmer or fatter.

DIFFUSION The spreading out of the molecules of a gas or liquid.

Examples. The diffusion of dissolved foods through the protoplasm of a cell.

The diffusion of a smell inside a closed room.

DIGESTION The conversion of insoluble food into simpler soluble chemicals in the gut of an animal. The molecules of food are broken down with the help of enzymes, and the soluble chemicals which are produced are absorbed by the walls of the gut and transferred to the blood.

DIODE A component which allows the flow of electric current in one direction but resists it (does not allow it) in the other.

Circuit diagram symbol

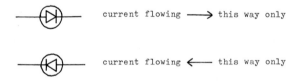

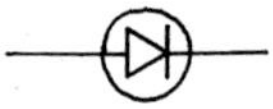

current flowing → this way only

current flowing ← this way only

DISEASE Something which alters or spoils the normal health or growth of an organism. Some of the causes of disease are (a) poor nutrition; (b) too much or too little production of hormones; (c) smoking, drug abuse or too much drinking of alcohol; (d) infections (bacteria, viruses, etc.); (e) inheriting from a previous generation, etc.

DISPERSAL The carrying or spreading of plant seeds by the wind, or by birds, animals, etc.

DISSOLVE A substance dissolves in a liquid when the molecules of the substance spread throughout the liquid. The result is a solution.

Example. Sodium chloride (common salt) dissolves in water to make brine (a solution).

DISTILLATION Boiling a liquid to form a gas, and then condensing the gas to form a liquid (called the distillate). Distillation is often used to separate a mixture of substances having different boiling points. It is a method of purifying liquid substances.

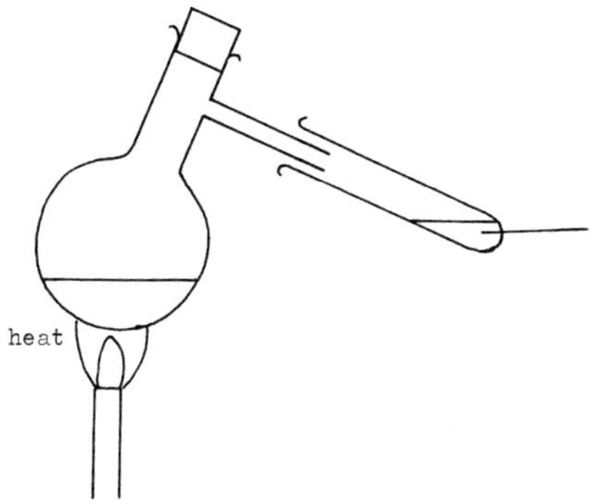

DISTILLED WATER Water which has been purified by distillation.

DISTRIBUTION The way in which things are spread out in nature. A distribution map shows the places where a certain species of plant or animal, etc., lives, and often shows how many live in each place.

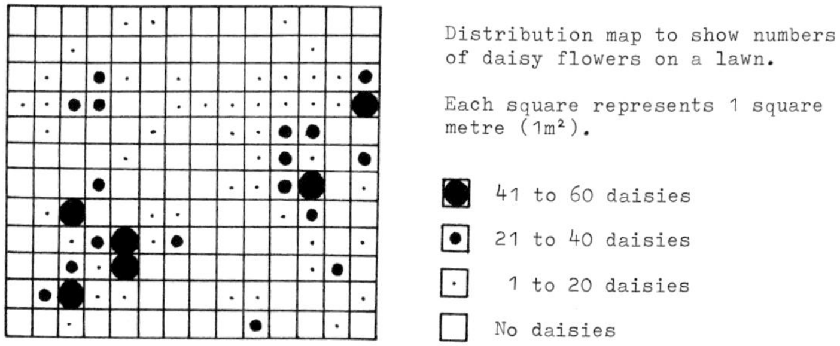

Distribution map to show numbers of daisy flowers on a lawn.
Each square represents 1 square metre (1m²).
41 to 60 daisies
21 to 40 daisies
1 to 20 daisies
No daisies

DNA The most important substance in a chromosome. Short for deoxyribonucleic acid (pr. dee-oxi-rybo-newk-lee-ik).

DORSAL At the back of an animal.
Example. A dorsal fin of a fish is a fin on the back of the fish.

DPDT SWITCH Double-pole double-throw switch. A switch consisting of two single-pole double-throw switches coupled together.

DRUG A chemical (e.g. aspirin, paracetamol, penicillin, morphine, sulpha drug) which is used for treating illnesses. Some people get pleasure from using drugs (e.g. alcohol, tobacco, heroin, cannabis, LSD, Ecstasy) but this can be highly dangerous as these drugs can cause illness, drug addiction (when the person cannot stop taking the drug) and sometimes death.

DUCTILE A ductile substance is one which can be drawn out into a wire without breaking. Many metals (e.g. copper) are ductile substances.

DYNAMO A device or machine for converting kinetic energy into electrical energy. A dynamo consists of a magnet with coils of wire which can rotate between its poles. When the coils are rotated, an electric current flows in the wire.

EARTH One of the planets of the solar system. It orbits the Sun every $365\frac{1}{4}$ days (1 year) at a distance of about 150 000 000 km (about 93 000 000 miles).

It is in the shape of a geoid, or oblate spheroid, which is almost a sphere (round ball shape) but is flatter at the north and south poles, and fatter at the Equator, because of centrifugal force. Its diameter across the Equator is about 12756 km (7926 miles) and its circumference round the Equator is about 40075 km (24900 miles).

The Earth spins round once, from west to east, every 24 hours (1 day). It is surrounded by an atmosphere consisting of air and is the only planet on which life is known to exist.

ECLIPSE An eclipse of the <u>Sun</u> happens when the Moon passes exactly between the Sun and the Earth, hiding all (a total eclipse) or part (a partial eclipse) of the Sun's disc.

An eclipse of the <u>Moon</u> happens when the Earth passes exactly between the Sun and the Moon, hiding all (a total eclipse) or part (a partial eclipse) of the Moon's disc.

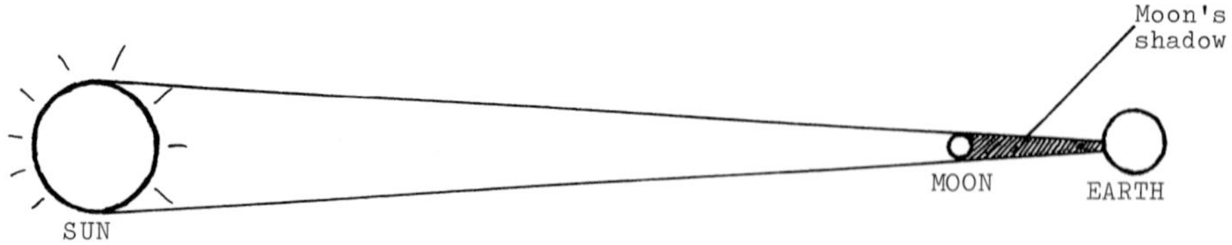

An eclipse of the Sun (simplified diagram not drawn to scale)

ECOLOGY The part of biology which deals with the relationships between organisms and their environments.

EGG (1) A round or oval object laid by some animals, e.g. birds, fishes, insects, reptiles, etc., during reproduction. A fertilised egg contains an embryo and its food store (and sometimes other substances) inside a membrane. Some eggs, e.g. birds' eggs, also have a shell on the outside of the membrane.

Hens' eggs sold for food are unfertilised.

(2) A female gamete, produced in the ovary of a mammal.

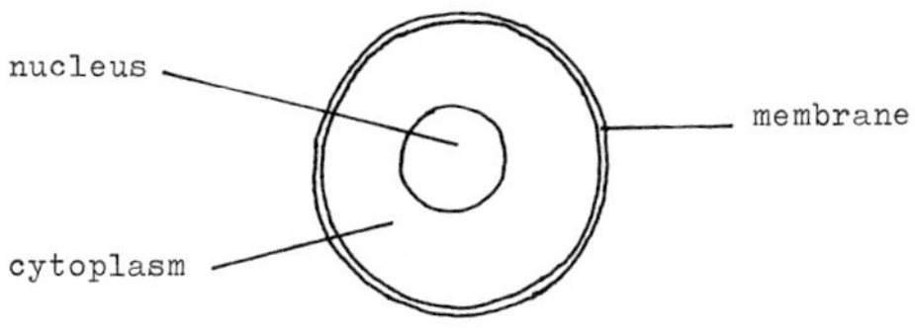

Human egg
(200X real length)

ELASTIC LIMIT The greatest stress which can be put on something without permanently changing its shape.

Example. The point of stretching of a spring beyond which the spring will not return to its original shape, and no longer extends in proportion to its load.

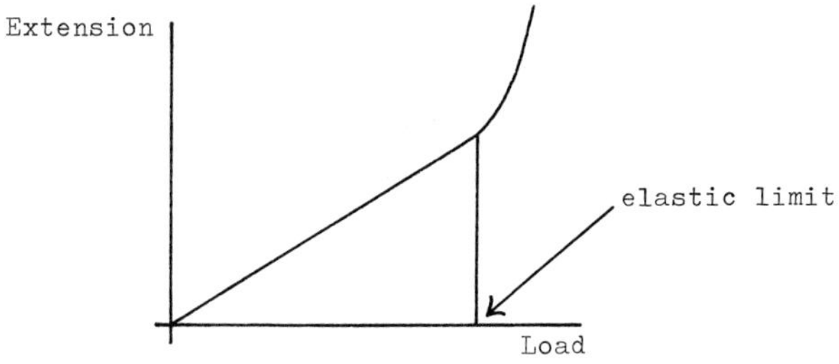

Graph showing the extension (stretching) of a spring with an increasing load

ELECTRICITY An electric charge or current.

Static electricity consists of a stationary (staying still) electric charge on an object, e.g. the charge which a fountain pen possesses after it has been rubbed against a cloth.

Current electricity consists of a flow of electrons through a conductor, e.g. the flow of electrons through a wire from a cell to a lamp.

ELECTRIC MOTOR A device or machine for converting electrical energy into kinetic energy. An electric motor consists of a magnet with coils of wire which can rotate between its poles. When an electric current is passed through the wire, the coils rotate.

Circuit diagram symbol 

ELECTROCHEMICAL SERIES See REACTIVITY SERIES.

ELECTROMOTIVE FORCE (EMF) See VOLTAGE.

ELECTRON A negatively-charged particle which occurs in all atoms. The electrons in an atom move about in the space surrounding the nucleus. The atom of each different element contains a special number of electrons (e.g. hydrogen 1 electron, carbon 6 electrons, silver 47 electrons, etc.).

An electric current is a flow of electrons through a conductor.

ELECTRONICS The science which deals with electrical circuits containing such devices as diodes, transistors, logic gates, etc., which control the flow of electrons.

ELEMENT The simplest kind of substance. A substance which consists of atoms all of the same kind. There are over 100 different elements from which all other substances are made. When two or more elements combine chemically they form a compound.

Elements are either metals (e.g. iron, copper, aluminium) or non-metals (e.g. oxygen, sulphur, carbon).

Some common elements with their symbols

Metals	Non-metals
Aluminium (Al)	Carbon (C)
Calcium (Ca)	Chlorine (Cl)
Chromium (Cr)	Helium (He)
Copper (Cu)	Hydrogen (H)
Gold (Au)	Iodine (I)
Iron (Fe)	Nitrogen (N)
Lead (Pb)	Oxygen (O)
Magnesium (Mg)	Phosphorus (P)
Mercury (Hg)	Silicon (Si)
Potassium (K)	Sulphur (S)
Silver (Ag)	
Tin (Sn)	
Zinc (Zn)	

ELLIPSE The elongated or squashed circle shape of the orbits of planets round the Sun.

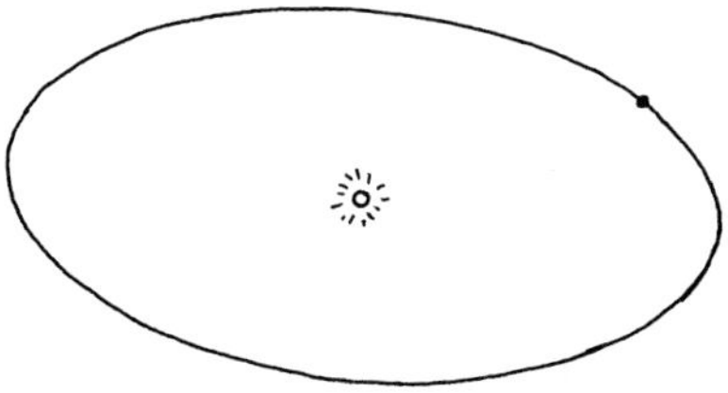

EMBRYO An animal before it is born or hatched, or a plant in an early stage of development.

EMF Electromotive force. See VOLTAGE.

ENDOTHERMIC An endothermic reaction is one which absorbs thermal (heat) energy.

ENERGY The ability or capacity to do work, e.g. to make something move, change shape or direction, change from solid to liquid or liquid to gas, increase in temperature, etc.

Different kinds of energy include chemical, electrical, thermal (heat), kinetic, potential, radiation (light, etc.), sound and strain (spring).

ENVIRONMENT The surroundings in which an organism lives.

ENZYME A kind of protein which acts as a catalyst to speed up chemical reactions in an organism, either inside or outside the cells of the organism. Enzyme names often end in -ase.

Example. An enzyme called amylase in saliva (spit) speeds up the change of starch into sugar.

EPITHELIAL TISSUE (pr. eppi-thee-lee-al) An animal tissue made of a sheet of closely-packed cells covering or lining a surface. Also called epithelium.

Example. Human cheek cells on the inside of the mouth.

ETHANOL Also called ethyl alcohol. The kind of alcohol found in alcoholic drinks, methylated spirit, etc. Used as a solvent and for making other chemicals.

EVAPORATING BASIN A shallow bowl usually used for evaporating the water from a solution of a salt, leaving behind the salt crystals.

Usually drawn 

EVAPORATION The turning of a liquid into a vapour.

EVERGREEN A tree or shrub which bears leaves all through the year, e.g. laurel, holly. Trees which are not evergreens are deciduous trees.

EVOLUTION (1) The gradual changing of the features of organisms through long periods of time to produce species which are in some way unlike the original ones.

(2) The producing of a gas during a chemical reaction.
Example. The evolution of carbon dioxide when a carbonate reacts with an acid.

EXCRETION Getting rid of waste (unwanted matter) formed by chemical reactions in a plant or animal, e.g. urinating, sweating.

EXOSKELETON A skeleton or hard protective structure on the outside of some animals.
Example. A crab has an exoskeleton.

EXOTHERMIC An exothermic reaction is one which produces thermal (heat) energy.

EXPAND Become larger. Many substances expand when their temperature rises.

EXTINCT An extinct organism is a kind of organism of which there are no longer any living examples in the world.
Examples. Dinosaurs (extinct reptiles), dodo (extinct bird).

FAECES (pr. fee-seez) A mixture of food remains and other chemicals which forms in the large intestine and leaves the body through the anus.

FAMILY A division of an order. See CLASSIFICATION.

FAT One of many different energy-rich compounds of carbon, hydrogen and oxygen (though the atoms are not arranged in the same pattern as in carbohydrates).
Fats are produced by plants and animals and are very similar to organic oils but they are solid (not liquid like oils) at normal temperatures.
Examples. Butter (from milk), lard (from pigs).

FERMENTATION A chemical reaction in which an organic compound (e.g. a carbohydrate) is converted into other substances by the action of a living organism (e.g. bacterium, yeast, enzyme).

Example. The glucose (sugar) in grapes is converted into ethanol (ethyl alcohol) and carbon dioxide by the action of an enzyme in the skin of the grapes during the production of wine.

FERN A non-flowering plant, with a stem and roots, which reproduces by means of spores.

FERTILE Fertile soil (having good fertility) is soil containing plant nutrients and therefore able to produce good crops.
A fertile seed, egg, etc., is one which is able to grow and develop.

FERTILISATION The fusion (or joining together) of a male gamete and a female gamete to form a zygote.

FERTILISER A substance, often containing nitrogen, which is added to soil to make it produce more or better crops.

FETUS See FOETUS.

FIBRE (1) The cellulose part of the human diet (plant tissues such as lettuce leaves, bran, etc.) which is mostly undigested but is valuable because it exercises the muscles of the intestines. Also called roughage.
(2) A long thread of material, such as plant or animal tissue.

FILTER FUNNEL A funnel which holds filter paper for filtration.

Usually drawn

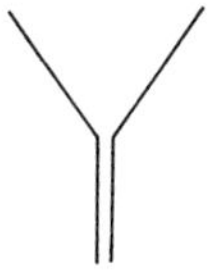

FILTRATION Passing a mixture of a liquid and an insoluble solid through a filter (e.g. blotting paper) so that the insoluble solid stays behind in the filter. A method for separating an insoluble substance from a soluble one (e.g. chalk and salt). The liquid which passes through the filter is the filtrate.

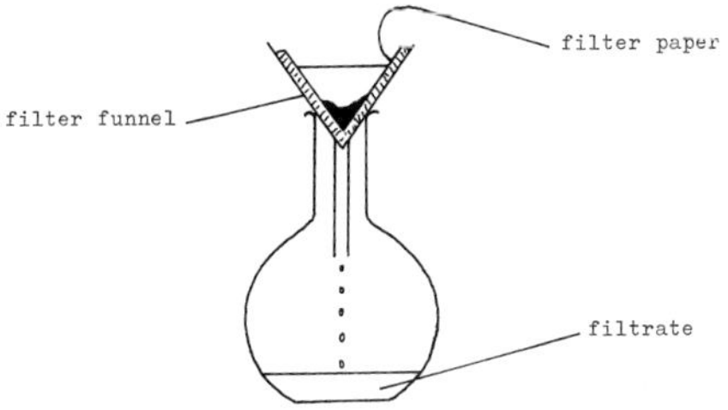

FISH One of a class of aquatic, cold-blooded vertebrate animals with gills, and often fins and a scaly skin.

FLAMMABLE (or **INFLAMMABLE**) A flammable substance or material is one which catches fire easily, e.g. petrol.

'Flammable' and 'inflammable' both mean the same thing.

FLASK A bottle-shaped or bulb-shaped container, often with a narrow neck, used for holding or heating liquids.

Usually drawn

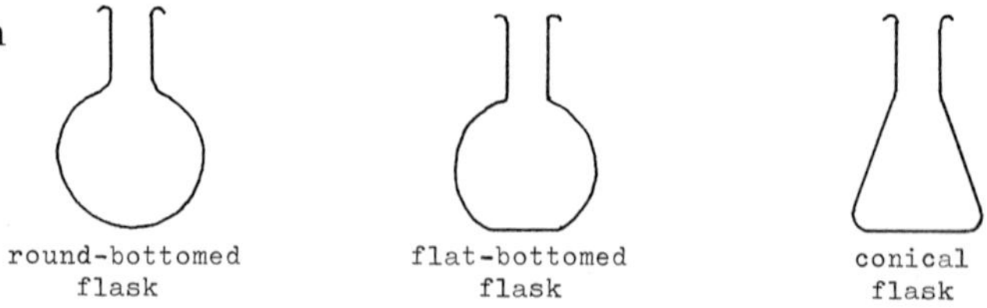

FLOWER The reproductive parts of a flowering plant, consisting of petals, sepals, ovary, style, stigma, stamen, anther, etc.

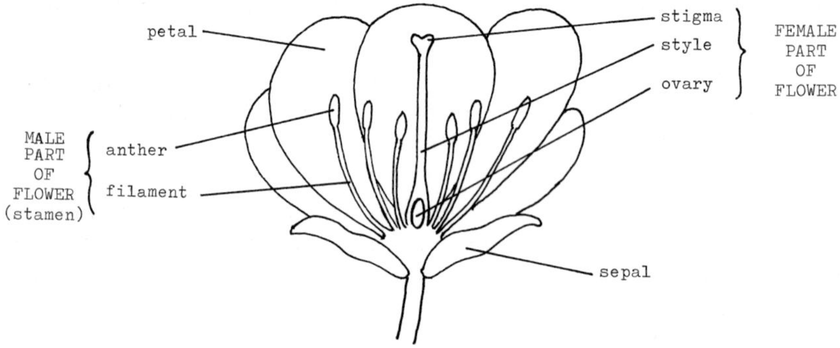

FOETUS (pr. feet-us) An embryo of an animal when it has developed enough to look like the animal. A human embryo becomes a foetus about two months after it is first formed. Foetus is sometimes spelt fetus.

FOOD CHAIN A 'chain' or series of living things in which each member depends for food, and therefore energy, on the member below it in the chain. The chain begins with a producer (plant life) and ends with a top carnivore.

Example.
rose plant → greenfly → ladybird → shrew → badger
(i.e. greenflies feed on rose plants, ladybirds feed on greenflies, etc.)

FOOD WEB A combination of different food chains in the same community. A food web is often shown as a diagram.

Example.

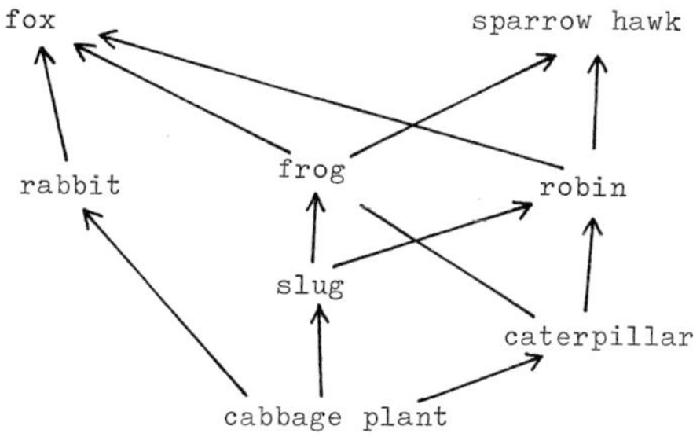

e.g. caterpillar eats cabbage plant, frog eats slug, etc.

FORCE Something, such as a 'push' or a 'pull', which can change the rate or direction of motion (or movement) of an object.

Force is usually measured in newtons (N).

FORMULA A short way of writing the name of an element or compound (or one molecule of an element or compound) by using symbols. A formula also shows how many, and what sort of, atoms make up the molecule of the element or compound.

Example. The formula for sodium sulphate is Na_2SO_4, showing that its molecule contains 2 atoms of sodium (Na), 1 atom of sulphur (S) and 4 atoms of oxygen (O).

FOSSIL The remains, usually preserved in rock, of an organism (plant, animal, etc.) which lived thousands or millions of years ago. Fossils may be bones or shells of the original organism, or petrified (turned to rock) parts of the organism, or a cast made by the shape of the organism.

Example. Ammonite (prehistoric sea animal).

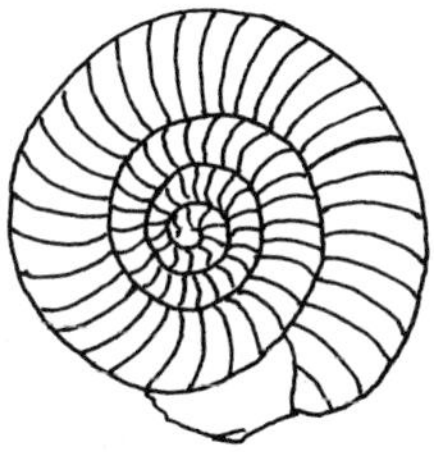

FOSSIL FUEL A substance in the Earth's crust, formed from the remains of prehistoric (living thousands or millions of years ago) plants or animals, and burned as a fuel, e.g. coal, oil, peat, natural gas. Fossil fuels contain mainly carbon (e.g. coal) or hydrocarbons (e.g. natural gas).

FRACTIONAL DISTILLATION Boiling a mixture of liquids with different boiling points and then condensing each separate liquid at a different temperature. Fractional distillation is usually done in a fractionating column or tower. Each of the separate condensed liquids is called a fraction. This process is used for producing different substances from crude oil (e.g. petrol, paraffin, diesel fuel, etc.) and for separating the different gases from air which has first been liquified.

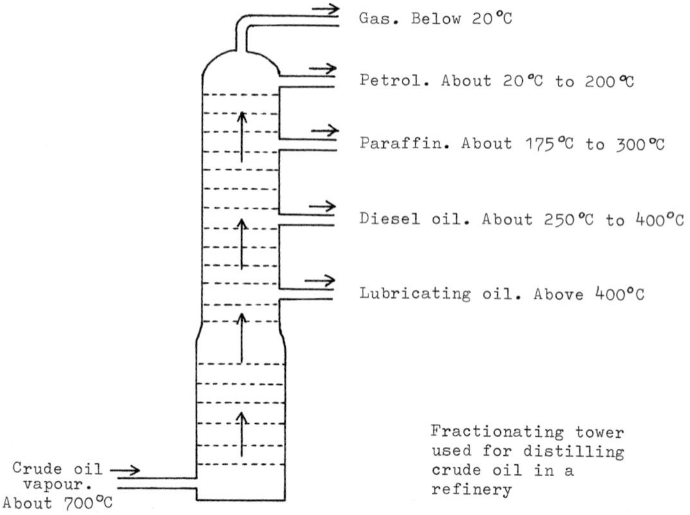

Fractionating tower used for distilling crude oil in a refinery

FREEZE A liquid freezes when it becomes so cold that its molecules, which move freely in the liquid, slow down and link together, making the liquid turn solid.

Example. Water freezes to become ice.

FREEZING POINT The temperature at which a liquid freezes (becomes cold enough to turn into a solid). This is the same temperature as the melting point.

Example. The freezing point of water is 0°C, the temperature at which water (liquid) freezes to become ice (solid).

FREQUENCY The number of times something happens in a certain length of time. Frequency is usually the number of vibrations, cycles, etc., happening in one second. Frequency is measured in hertz (Hz) (number of vibrations, etc. divided by time (seconds)).

FRICTION A force resisting the movement of two surfaces in contact with each other. Normally, the rougher the surfaces are, the greater the friction. Friction is not a form of energy, but it can be used to convert kinetic energy into thermal (heat) energy, e.g. by rubbing hands together.

FRUIT A plant ovary after fertilisation and ripening. A fruit contains one or more seeds.

Examples.

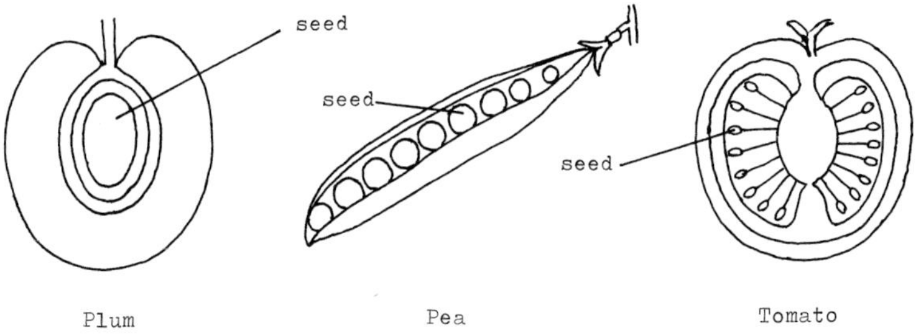

FUEL A substance that is used for producing energy, usually in the form of thermal (heat) energy, by burning or by nuclear reaction.

FULCRUM The pivot, or turning point, of a lever.

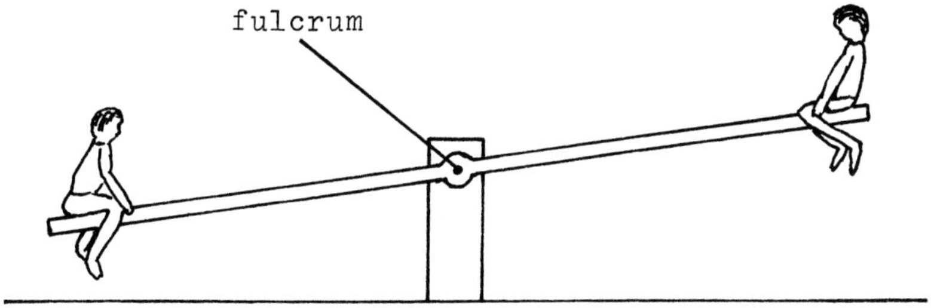

FULL RANGE INDICATOR A mixture of dyes which will change colour according to the pH of the liquid to which it is added. The colours are approximately

pH 1	..	red	strong	ACID
pH 3	..	pink	↕	ACID
pII 4	..	orange	weak	ACID
pH 7	..	green		NEUTRAL
pH 9	..	blue	weak	ALKALI
			↕	ALKALI
pH 11 - 14	..	purple	strong	ALKALI

FUNGUS A member of the Fungi kingdom which includes mushrooms, yeasts, moulds, etc. A fungus is a parasite or a saprophyte and reproduces asexually by spores. The spores are produced in great quantities and are released into the air. Any which find suitable conditions grow into new examples of the original fungus.

Example. Common Ink Cap

☠ DANGER. Some fungi are <u>deadly poisonous</u>.

FUSE A component used to prevent too high a current flowing through a circuit. It is made of a kind of resistance wire which melts at a low temperature. If the current becomes too high, the wire heats up and melts. This makes a gap, breaks the circuit and switches off the current, preventing damage or fire anywhere else in the circuit.

Circuit diagram symbol 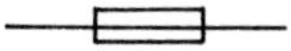

GALAXY A collection of millions of stars forming a spiral or other shape. The spiral galaxy to which the Sun belongs (our own galaxy) is called the Galaxy (with a capital G).

One of our nearest neighbouring galaxies (M 31), which is 2 200 000 light years away from us, can be seen in the constellation of Andromeda.

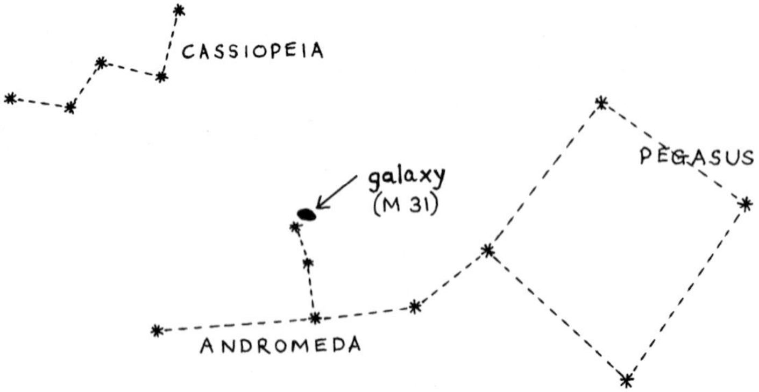

GAMETE (pr. gam-eet or gum-eet) A reproductive cell with (normally) a single set of unpaired chromosomes.
Examples. Sperm, ovum (in animals).
Pollen, ovule (in a flowering plant).

GAS A substance which is too hot to be a liquid or a solid. A substance is a gas when its temperature is above its boiling point.
A gas has no fixed volume or shape. If it is poured into an enclosed container it will diffuse (spread out) to fill the container.
The molecules of a gas move about freely at high speeds.

GATE Another name for a logic circuit, e.g. AND gate, NOR gate, etc.

GENE (pr. jeen) The part of a chromosome that decides which features of an organism pass from one generation to the next.
Example. In a human being, a certain gene can give you blue eyes.

GENUS (pr. jeen-us) A division of a family. See CLASSIFICATION. The plural is genera (pr. jenn-er-a).

GERMINATION The first stage in the growth of a seed or spore.
Germination can happen only when the conditions are right, e.g. enough moisture, enough warmth, etc. The germination of a plant seed can be detected when a root or shoot begins to form.

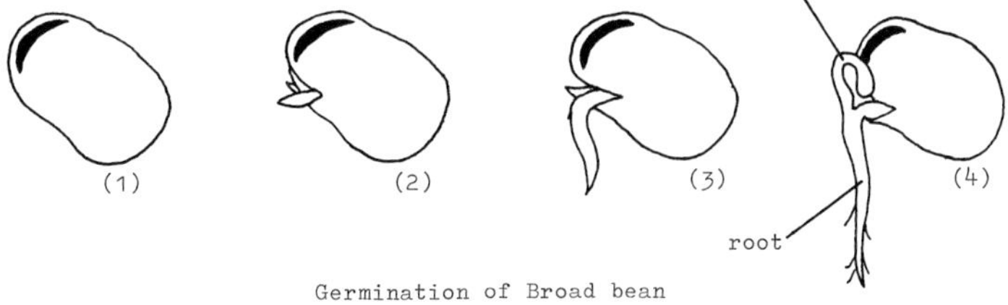

Germination of Broad bean

GESTATION (pr. jest-ay-shn) The development of a mammal between fertilisation of the egg and the birth of the young animal.

GILLS (1) The organs through which fish and many other water creatures breathe. The gills take in oxygen from the water and release the carbon dioxide produced by respiration.

(2) The structures on the underneath of the cap of some kinds of fungus, e.g. mushroom, which produce spores for reproduction.

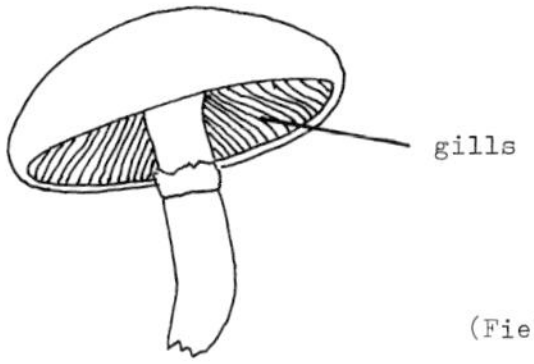

(Field mushroom)

GLAND An organ which produces a special chemical needed by the body. Examples. Sweat glands, liver.

GLOBAL WARMING There is evidence that the Earth's atmosphere is gradually becoming warmer. Many scientists believe that this is because of extra amounts of carbon dioxide, methane and other gases which have been produced by burning fossil fuels (which releases carbon dioxide and other gases), destroying rain forests which normally absorb carbon dioxide, etc. See GREENHOUSE EFFECT.

GLUCOSE A kind of sugar found in fruit and honey. It is also produced from carbon dioxide and water by plants during photosynthesis, and from other carbohydrates in the human body during digestion.

GOLD An element. A soft, yellow, shiny, dense metal which is very ductile and malleable. It is used (as an alloy with other metals) for making jewellery. Very thin sheets of gold are called gold leaf.

The amount of gold in a gold alloy is measured in carats (the number of parts of gold in 24 parts of alloy), e.g. 9 carat gold is $^{9}/_{24}$ gold.

The symbol for gold is Au (from its old name aurum).

GRAM A unit of mass. The symbol for grams is g (not gm or gms).

1000 milligrams	=	1 gram	(1000mg = 1g)
1000 grams	=	1 kilogram	(1000g = 1kg)

GRAPHITE A black, crystalline form of carbon. Graphite is unusual because, although it is a non-metal, it is an excellent conductor of electricity. It is used for making electrical components, pencil 'lead', etc.

GRAVITY The force exerted by one object on another because of its mass. The greater the mass of the object, the greater the gravity it exerts. The gravity of the Earth causes objects less massive than itself to fall towards it. Gravity acts towards the centre of the Earth, which is why it always seems to pull you down.

GREENHOUSE EFFECT The warming of the Earth's surface and lower parts of the atmosphere because of carbon dioxide, water vapour and other gases which allow radiation energy (from the Sun) in but do not allow all of it out again, like the glass in a greenhouse. The greenhouse effect keeps the temperature at the Earth's surface at a suitable level for life to exist, but some scientists think that, because of the extra carbon dioxide and other gases being produced, especially by human activity, the temperature will rise in future years and cause problems.

GULLET Another name for oesophagus. See OESOPHAGUS.

GUT Also called alimentary canal. The tube in an animal leading from its mouth to its anus. Food is digested and absorbed in the gut.

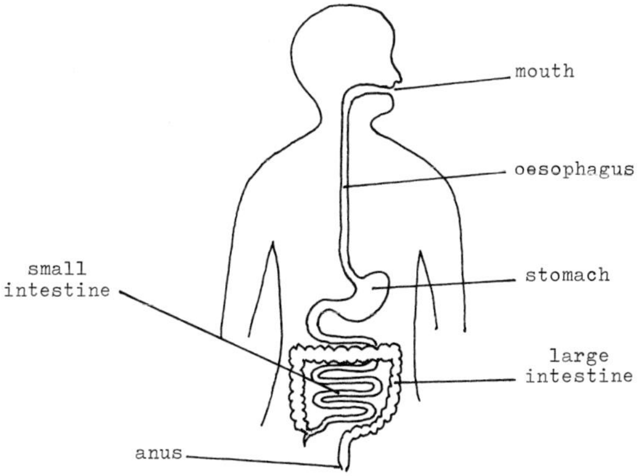

HABITAT The natural place where an organism lives.

HAEMOGLOBIN (pr. heem-o-glow-bin) The red substance in red blood cells which is responsible for transporting oxygen.

HEART The organ which pumps blood round the body. The blood leaves the heart through blood vessels (tubes) called arteries and returns through veins. See CIRCULATION.

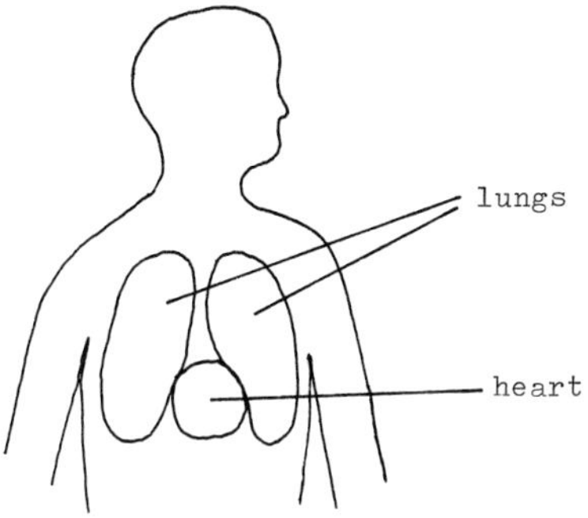

HEAT When a substance or object is heated it is given more thermal energy, often resulting in expansion, melting or evaporation. See THERMAL ENERGY.

HELIUM (pr. hee-lee-um) An element. A light, unreactive gas (non-metal) without colour or smell. As it is less dense than air, it is used for filling balloons. See INERT GAS.

HERBIVORE An animal which eats grass or other plant life. A herbivore is usually a primary consumer.

Examples. Rabbit, cow.

HIBERNATE Sleep through the winter. Animals which hibernate include hedgehog, bat, grass snake, frog, etc.

HISTOGRAM A graph made of rectangles to show frequency distribution (how many there are of different sizes of things).

Example. A histogram to show heights, to the nearest centimetre, of Norway spruce trees in a plantation.

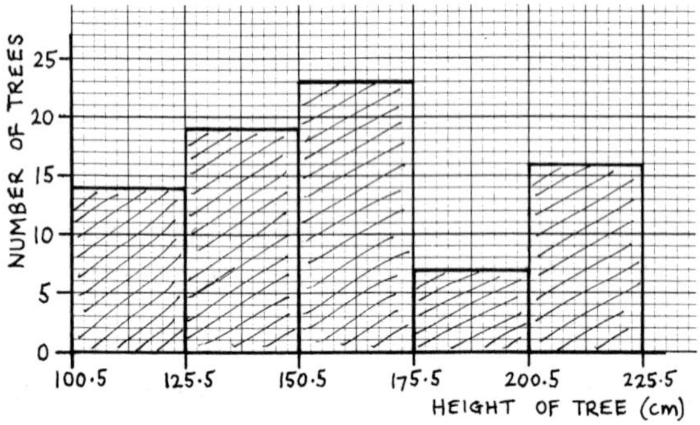

e.g. There are 19 trees with heights from 126cm to 150cm.

HIV Human Immuno-deficiency Virus. A virus which can cause the disease AIDS. It can be passed from one human being to another either by sexual intercourse, or from a mother to an unborn baby, or through the blood (by injections, etc.).

HORMONE A special substance produced by a gland of an animal and carried by the blood to the part of the body which needs it.
Examples. Adrenaline, insulin.

HOST The organism on or in which a parasite lives.

HUMANE TRAP A trap for catching animals without hurting them.

HYDRATED A hydrated salt is a salt which contains water of crystallisation.
Example. Blue copper sulphate is a hydrated salt.

HYDROCARBON A compound containing only carbon and hydrogen, e.g. methane (CH_4), butane (C_4H_{10}), etc.

Crude oil and natural gas are made mainly from a mixture of hydrocarbons.

HYDROELECTRIC POWER Electrical energy produced from the kinetic energy of moving water, usually by making the water flow through turbines in a hydroelectric power station. The turbines are normally built into a dam which crosses a river or tidal estuary. The water turns the blades of the turbines which operate dynamos to produce an electric current.

HYDROGEN An element. A flammable gas (non-metal) without colour or smell. It has the lowest density of all known substances. It combines with other elements to form compounds such as water, acids, hydrocarbons, carbohydrates, etc.

If a flame is held at the mouth of a test-tube containing hydrogen, the hydrogen will burn with a squeaky popping sound.

The symbol for hydrogen is H.

HYPOTHESIS (pr. hy-poth-iss-iss) An explanation, which may or may not turn out to be correct, of facts found by experiment or observation.

IMMISCIBLE (pr. im-iss-i-bl) Two (or more) liquids are immiscible if they will not mix together to form one single liquid, e.g. water and oil.

INDICATOR A substance which changes colour when mixed with liquids of different pH values, and so can be used to indicate how acidic or alkaline the liquid is. Some common indicators are full-range indicator, Universal indicator, litmus, methyl orange and phenolphthalein.

INERT GAS One of a group of non-metal elements (helium, neon, argon, krypton, xenon and radon) which are unreactive gases without colour or smell. The first five of these are found in small quantities in the air.

Helium (He) is used for filling balloons as it has a very low density and is not flammable. Argon (Ar) is used to fill electric light bulbs. Neon (Ne), krypton (Kr) and xenon (Xe) are used in various kinds of fluorescent lighting. Radon (Rn) is radioactive and can cause illness from radiation, but is also used for treating certain diseases.

Inert gases are also called noble gases.

INORGANIC Not organic. Containing no carbon. Not produced by organisms.

INSECT One of a class of arthropods. Most insects have a body divided into three main parts (head, thorax and abdomen), an exoskeleton, six (3 pairs of) legs, two antennae and two pairs of wings. The class includes flies, wasps, bees, ants, butterflies, moths and others.

Insects are the largest class of animals, with over 1 million species already known and many more yet to be identified.

Examples.

Black ant

House fly

7-spot ladybird

INSECTICIDE Something (usually a chemical) which is used for killing insects.

INSOLUBLE Not dissolving. A substance is insoluble in a liquid if it does not dissolve in the liquid.

Example. Sulphur is insoluble in water.

INSULATOR A substance which is a poor conductor of electricity or thermal (heat) energy.

Most non-metals are insulators - with the important exception of graphite, a form of carbon, which is a very good conductor.

Examples. Plastic for covering copper wires in electric cables, thus preventing shocks and ensuring that the wires do not touch and short-circuit.

Glass fibre in lofts of houses to reduce loss of thermal (heat) energy through the roof.

INTERNAL ENERGY See THERMAL ENERGY.

INTESTINES (pr. in-tess-tinz) The part of the gut between the stomach and the anus. The upper part is the small intestine and the lower part is the large intestine.

INVERTEBRATE An animal which has no backbone.

Examples. Earthworm, snail, octopus.

IODINE (pr. I-o-deen) An element. A black, shiny, crystalline, solid non-metal which forms a brown solution in ethanol. Iodine solution can be used as a test for starch; when mixed with starch, the brown solution turns a very dark blue - almost black.

The symbol for iodine is I.

IRON An element. A grey metal which rusts (forming iron oxide) when it is in contact with both air and water. Iron is used in various forms, such as cast iron, wrought iron and steel.

Iron filings are particles of iron.

The symbol for iron is Fe (from its old name ferrum).

ISOBAR An imaginary line, or a line drawn on a weather map, joining all the points in a weather system which have equal air pressure.

Example.

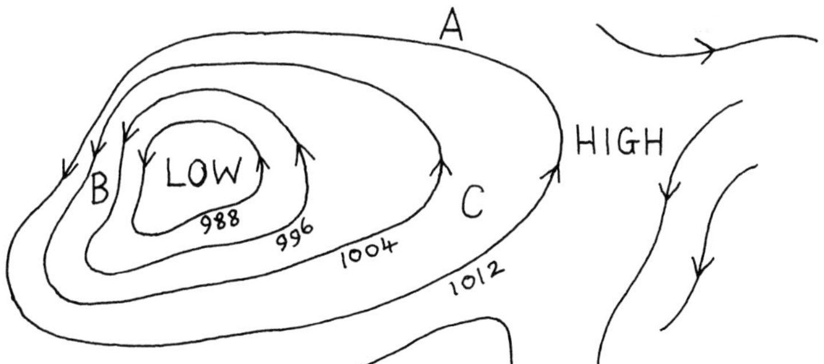

These lines are isobars. All the points on isobar A have a pressure of 1012 millibars (1012mb). Isobars in area B are close together, meaning strong winds. Isobars in area C are far apart, meaning light winds. In the Northern hemisphere (north of the Equator), winds go anticlockwise round a low pressure area, clockwise round a high pressure area. The opposite happens in the Southern hemisphere.

JOULE (pr. jool) A unit of work or energy. The amount of work done when a force of 1 newton moves a distance of 1 metre in the direction of the force. Named after the English scientist James P. Joule (born 1818, died 1889).

KEY A list of clues and answers for identifying an organism (finding out which species it is).

Example. Key for identifying thrushes.

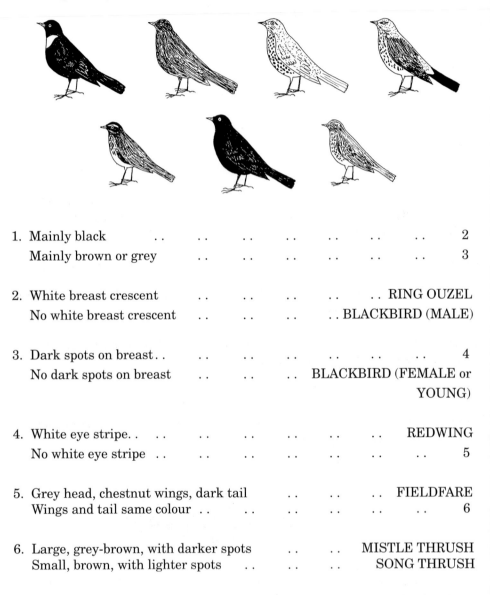

1. Mainly black 2
   Mainly brown or grey 3

2. White breast crescent .. .. RING OUZEL
   No white breast crescent .. .. BLACKBIRD (MALE)

3. Dark spots on breast.. 4
   No dark spots on breast .. .. .. BLACKBIRD (FEMALE or YOUNG)

4. White eye stripe.. .. .. REDWING
   No white eye stripe 5

5. Grey head, chestnut wings, dark tail .. .. .. FIELDFARE
   Wings and tail same colour 6

6. Large, grey-brown, with darker spots .. .. MISTLE THRUSH
   Small, brown, with lighter spots .. .. .. SONG THRUSH

To identify the bird correctly, look at 1. If the bird is mainly brown or grey, look at 3. If it has dark spots on its breast, look at 4, etc., until you come to the name of the correct bird.

KIDNEYS The two organs at either side of the spine which take out water, urea, salts and other waste substances from the blood and pass them as urine through the ureters to the bladder.

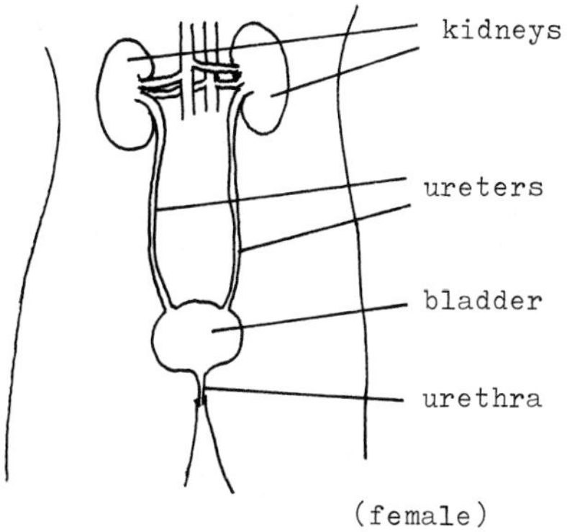

KINETIC ENERGY Motion energy. The energy which something has by moving. The faster an object moves, the greater is its kinetic energy.
Example. The energy of a sledge going down a slope.

KINGDOM One of the five basic groups to which all living things belong (see CLASSIFICATION).
The kingdoms are Animals, Plants, Fungi, Monera (including bacteria) and Protista (including single-celled algae).

LAMP A device which converts electrical energy (or sometimes chemical energy, as in an oil lamp) to light energy.

Circuit diagram symbol for electric lamp 

LARVA An insect after it has hatched from an egg and before it becomes a pupa or a fully-developed insect.

Example. Larva of Vapourer Moth.

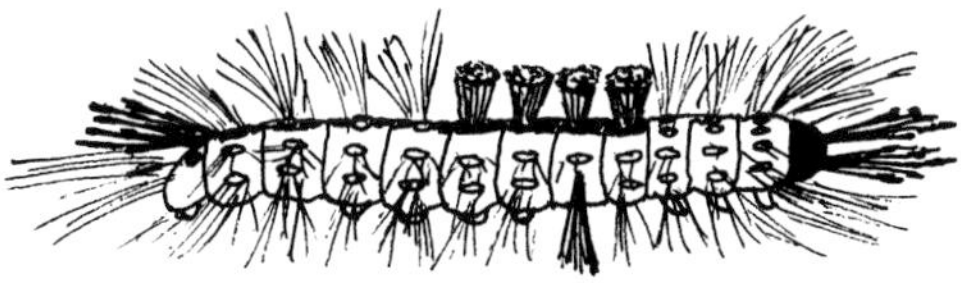

LDR Light-dependent resistor. A resistor which, when exposed to light, becomes a conductor and allows the flow of electric current. If the LDR receives no light, it resists the flow of current (does not allow it).

Circuit diagram symbol 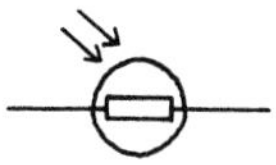

LEAD (pr. led) An element. A dense, malleable grey metal. It is used to make alloys (with tin) such as solder and pewter. Plates of lead are used in certain kinds of batteries, and sheet lead is sometimes used for roofing. Most of the compounds of lead are very poisonous.

The symbol for lead is Pb (from its old name plumbum which also gave us the word 'plumber' - someone who mended lead pipes).

LEAF The part of a plant which (a) absorbs carbon dioxide and light for photosynthesis; (b) releases oxygen, produced by photosynthesis, into the air; (c) releases water in the form of water vapour (transpiration).

LED Light-emitting diode. A diode which gives out light when an electric current is passed through it in the correct direction.

Circuit diagram symbol 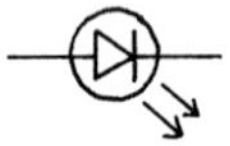

LENS A piece of material (often glass) which will either converge (bring together) or diverge (spread apart) rays of light.

A convex lens curves outwards and converges the rays.

A concave lens curves inwards and diverges the rays.

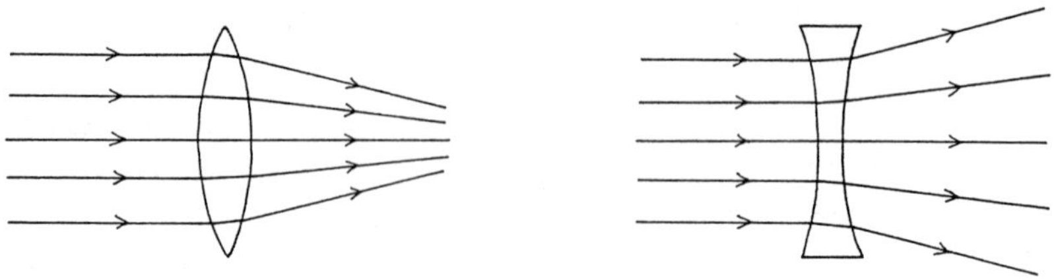

Convex lens   Concave lens

LEVER A bar which can be turned around a fixed point (or fulcrum).

LICHEN (pr. <u>ly</u>-kn or <u>lit</u>-shn) An organism formed by the symbiosis (interdependence) of an alga and a fungus.

Most lichens die in air containing pollutants, especially sulphur dioxide, so they are often a good indicator of how polluted the air is.

LIEBIG CONDENSER (pr. <u>lee</u>-big) A piece of apparatus for condensing a gas or vapour. The gas or vapour is passed along a tube which is surrounded by another tube containing running cold water. It is used mainly for distillation. Named after the German scientist Justus Liebig (born 1803, died 1873).

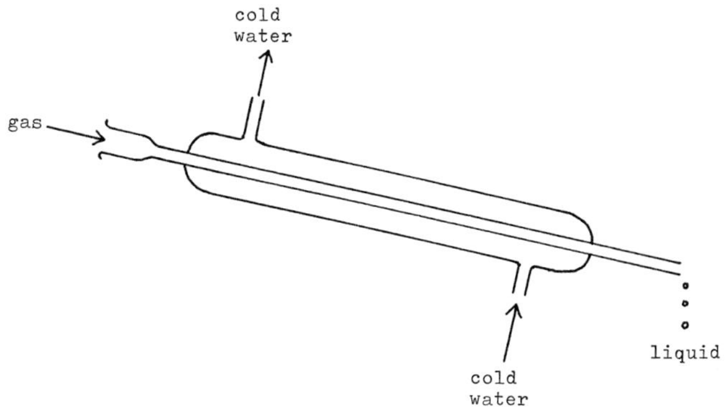

LIFE CYCLE The complete pattern of life of an organism, including all its changes, from a certain stage in one generation to the same stage in the next generation.

LIGHT A kind of radiation energy, travelling by wave movement, which can be seen. Light travels at 3×10^8 (300 000 000) metres per second, or 186 000 miles per second.

LIGHT YEAR A unit of length used for measuring distances of stars and galaxies. It is the distance travelled by light in one year.

1 light year ≏ 6×10^{12} miles (6 000 000 000 000 miles)

Example. The distance of Polaris (the Pole Star) is just over 400 light years ≏ 2.4×10^{15} miles (2 400 000 000 000 000 miles) from Earth. We see Polaris as it was just over 400 years ago (at about the time of the sailing of the Spanish Armada).

LIMB (pr. lim) An arm, leg or wing.

LIMESTONE A whitish-coloured rock consisting mainly of calcium carbonate, and formed from the remains of shells of small sea animals, particularly molluscs.

LIME WATER A colourless solution of calcium hydroxide in water. Lime water is used as a test for carbon dioxide, turning milky-white when carbon dioxide is bubbled through it (because insoluble calcium carbonate is formed).

LIQUID A substance which is too hot to be a solid, and too cold to be a gas. A substance is a liquid when its temperature is above its freezing point and below its boiling point.

When a liquid is poured into a container, it takes the shape of the container, sinking as far down as it can and forming a flat top (surface).

The molecules in a liquid are free to move in a restricted way, so although the volume of an amount of liquid stays the same, its shape can change easily.

LITMUS A purple indicator, made from a kind of lichen, which is turned red by an acid and blue by an alkali.

LIVER The 'chemical factory' of the body. The liver is a large gland (mammals have theirs in the abdomen) which

(a) removes old or useless red cells from the blood;

(b) produces bile (a green liquid) which is transported to the small intestine to help digestion;

(c) stores vitamins, iron compounds and sugar (in the form of glycogen);

(d) regulates the amount of sugar in the blood;

(e) turns poisonous chemicals in the body into harmless substances which are then transferred to the kidneys.

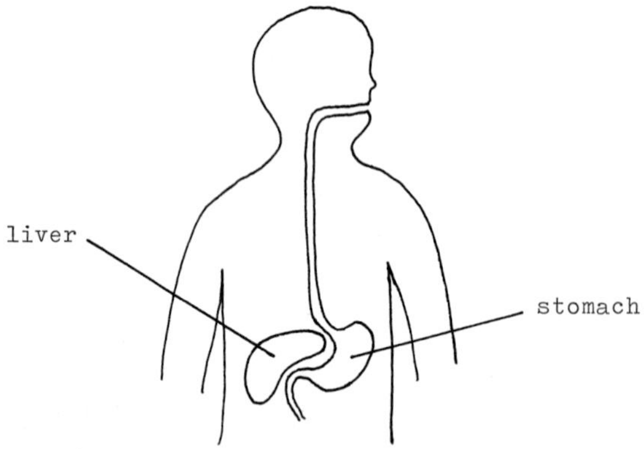

LOGIC CIRCUIT An electronic switching circuit (or decision maker) which has one or more inputs but only one output. Logic circuits include NOT, AND, NAND, OR and NOR. The voltage of the output depends on the voltages of the inputs and which kind of circuit is being used. Also called logic gate.

LUNGS The two organs in the chest (or thorax) which transfer oxygen from inhaled (breathed-in) air to the blood, and transfer carbon dioxide from the blood to exhaled (breathed-out) air.

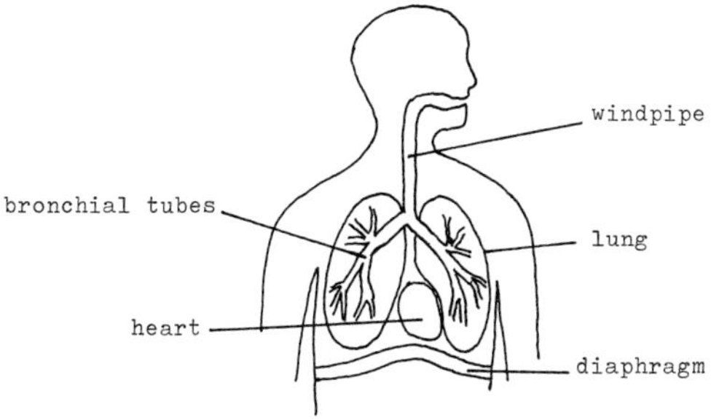

MAGNESIUM An element. A light, silvery reactive metal which becomes tarnished (forms a coating of magnesium oxide) when left in damp air. It burns with a bright white flame.

Magnesium is used for fireworks and signal flares and, alloyed with other metals, for making tools and car and aircraft parts, etc. It is essential for plant growth as it is one of the elements in chlorophyll.

The symbol for magnesium is Mg.

MAGNETIC FIELD A field (or lines) of force exerted by a magnet.

Example. The magnetic fields exerted by a bar magnet can be traced by sprinkling iron filings on a card held over a magnet. The pattern of iron filings shows the magnetic fields.

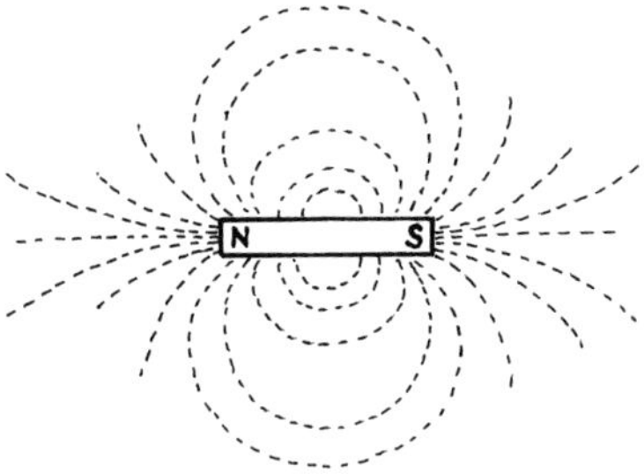

MALLEABLE (pr.<u>mal</u>-ee-ubbl) A malleable substance is one which can be hammered into sheets without breaking. Many metals (e.g. gold, lead) are malleable substances.

MAMMAL An animal which has mammary glands. In the female, the mammary glands develop, and produce milk for feeding the young.

Mammals are warm-blooded and normally have hair on their bodies.

Examples. Human being, dog, rabbit, whale.

MAMMARY GLANDS The glands in a female mammal which produce milk.

MANOMETER (pr. man-<u>om</u>-it-er) A piece of apparatus for measuring the pressure of a gas.

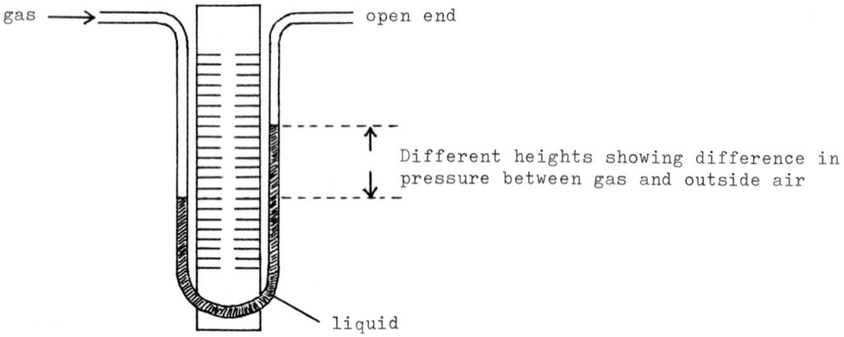

MASS A measurement of the amount of matter (material) in an object or collection of objects. The usual unit of mass is the gram.

1000 milligrams	= 1 gram	1000mg	= 1g
1000 grams	= 1 kilogram	1000g	= 1kg
1000 kilograms	= 1 tonne	1000kg	= 1t

Mass should not be confused with weight, although many people say 'weight' when they really mean 'mass'. The weight of something is the mass multiplied by the acceleration caused by gravity. Weight is usually measured in newtons (N).

To find the weight, in newtons, of an object on Earth, multiply the mass, in kilograms, by 10 (Multiplying by 9.8 gives a more accurate answer, but no-one would expect you to know this).

Example. The weight on Earth of a man with a mass of 75kg would be about 75 x 10 = 750N. However, on the Moon, the same man, with the same mass, would weigh only about 75 x 1.6 = 120N which is why heavy (massive) boots are needed for walking on the Moon.

MELT A solid melts when it gains enough thermal (heat) energy to cause its molecules to move so fast that they break apart from one another and start to flow around (become liquid).

MELTING POINT The temperature at which a solid becomes hot enough to melt and form a liquid. This is the same temperature as the freezing point.

Example. The melting point of paraffin wax (candle wax) is about 55°C, the temperature at which it melts and becomes a liquid.

MEMBRANE A sheet of tissue in an organism, often dividing one part of the organism from another, or lining an organ.

Example. Cell membrane which encloses the cytoplasm.

MENOPAUSE (pr. men-o-pawz) The time in the life of a female human being when menstruation stops, usually between the ages of 45 and 50 years.

MENSTRUAL CYCLE The regular pattern of events, between the ages of puberty and menopause, in the human female reproductive system. The cycle takes about one month, beginning with menstruation, when the uterus sheds its old lining. This lasts for about 3 to 7 days, after which the uterus begins to grow a new lining. About 14 days after the start of menstruation, ovulation occurs, when an egg (ovum) is released from the ovary. About 14 days after this, if the egg has not been fertilised, menstruation begins again.

MENSTRUATION (pr. men-stroo-ay-shn) The process by which the human female reproductive system gets rid of the old lining of the uterus, made of blood and membrane. This happens roughly once a month between the ages of puberty and menopause, and causes bleeding from the vagina. Menstruation stops during pregnancy; this is the first sign that most women have that they are expecting a baby. Menstruation is also called having a period.

MERCURY (1) An element. A dense, silvery metal that is liquid at normal temperatures. Mercury is used in thermometers, barometers, silent electric switches and some kinds of fluorescent lighting.

(☠ DANGER. MERCURY, MERCURY VAPOUR AND MERCURY COMPOUNDS ARE POISONOUS. DO NOT EXPERIMENT WITH MERCURY UNLESS YOU ARE STRICTLY SUPERVISED.)

The symbol for mercury is Hg (from its old name hydrargyrum which means 'liquid silver').

(2) One of the planets in the solar system. See PLANET.

METAL An element, or an alloy of elements, which usually (a) is shiny; (b) is ductile or malleable (or both); (c) is a good conductor of electricity and thermal (heat) energy; (d) forms a basic (alkaline) oxide; (e) is a solid at ordinary temperatures (except mercury which is a liquid).

Examples. Aluminium, magnesium, copper, gold.

METAMORPHOSIS (pr. met-a-mor-fer-sis)

Complete Metamorphosis A stage in the growth of some animals in which the new form looks completely different from the old.

Examples. Tadpole changing into frog.
Caterpillar changing into chrysalis, and chrysalis changing into butterfly.

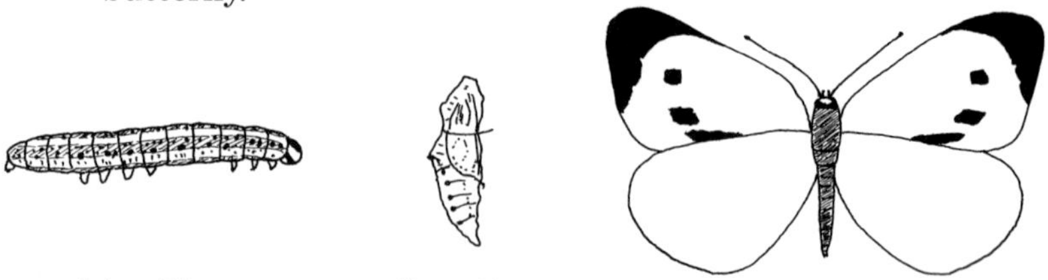

Caterpillar (larva) Chrysalis (pupa) Butterfly (fully-grown insect)

METAMORPHOSIS OF LARGE WHITE BUTTERFLY

Incomplete Metamorphosis Certain insects (such as grasshoppers, locusts, etc.) go through incomplete metamorphosis, during which there are several distinct stages of development, each of which is called an instar. At each stage the young insect looks slightly different.

METAMORPHOSIS OF GRASSHOPPER

METEOR A tiny piece of solid matter in space which enters the Earth's atmosphere (air) and burns up. Also called a shooting star.

Larger pieces of matter, which do not burn up completely, fall to the Earth as meteorites. A meteorite is made of stone or iron or a mixture of stone and iron.

METHYLATED SPIRIT A mixture consisting mainly of ethanol (ethyl alcohol). Used as a fuel and a solvent.

The purple methylated spirit sold in shops consists of ethanol (90%), methyl alcohol (to make it unfit to drink), pyridine (to give it a smell) and methyl blue (to colour it).

MICROSCOPE A device for producing magnified (larger) images of small objects. A microscope usually consists of one or more lenses.

MIGRATION The movement of animals from one habitat to another at certain times of the year.

Example. The migration of swallows from Africa to Northern Europe in the spring, and from Northern Europe to Africa in the autumn.

MILKY WAY Part of the Galaxy, or spiral system of stars, to which the Sun and other stars belong. It is made up of millions of stars and can be seen as a faint band across the night sky.

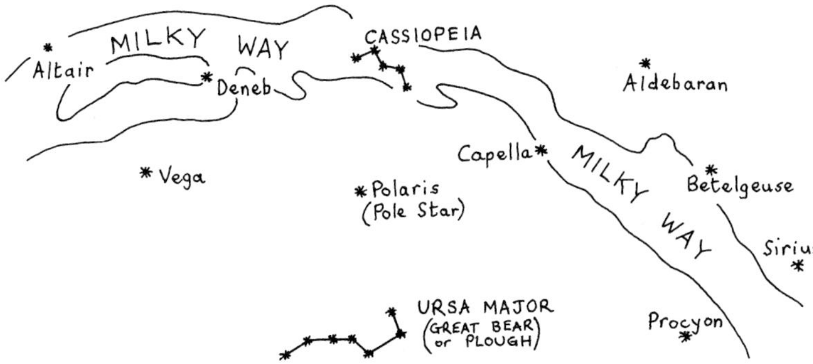

MINERAL A non-living substance found in nature. Minerals are usually solid and are often found as crystals. Many minerals are also ores from which metal elements can be extracted.

Examples. Pyrite (iron sulphide).

Malachite (copper carbonate and copper hydroxide).

Mineral oils are hydrocarbons usually obtained from crude oil (in an oil well).

Mineral salts are inorganic salts, such as nitrates. Solutions of mineral salts are absorbed from the soil by the roots of plants.

MIRROR A surface, such as a shiny metal, or glass painted with a shiny back, which is a good reflector of light.

Plane mirror. A flat mirror. The angle at which a ray of light strikes a plane mirror (the angle of incidence) is equal to the angle at which it is reflected (the angle of reflection).

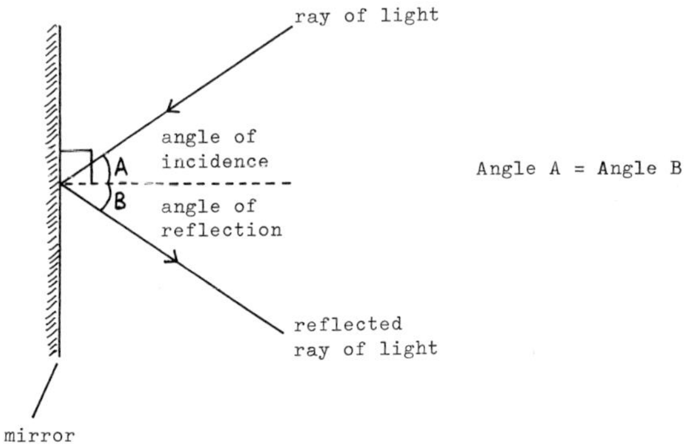

P.T.O. ➪

Curved mirror. A concave mirror curves inwards and converges (brings together) the rays of light. A convex mirror curves outwards and diverges (spreads apart) the rays.

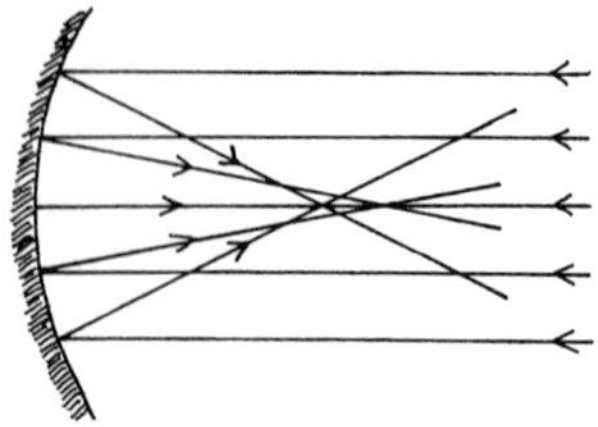

Concave mirror

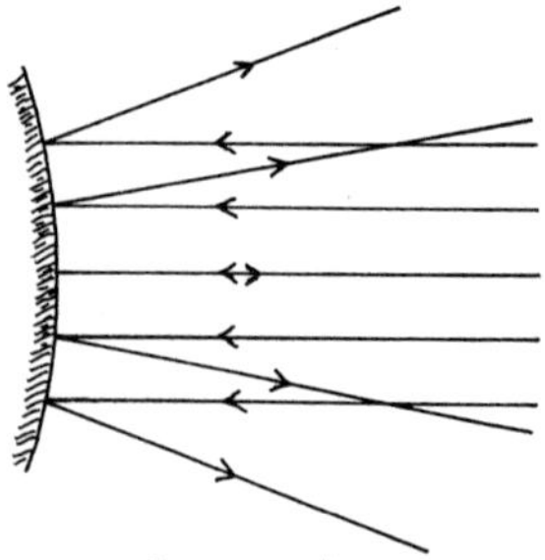

Convex mirror

MIXTURE A substance consisting of two or more other substances which have been stirred or mingled together but have not combined chemically. A mixture, unlike a compound, tends to stay rather like the things it is made from, and can be separated into its different substances by physical means (without a chemical reaction), such as filtration, distillation, etc.

Examples. Air is a mixture of gases.

Sea water is a mixture of solutions.

MOLECULE (pr. moll-ee-kyool) The smallest amount of a substance which retains the properties of the substance, and which can exist independently (on its own).

A molecule is sometimes a single atom, e.g. a molecule of helium, but it is more often made up of two or more atoms combined chemically.

A molecule of an element consists of atoms of the same kind, e.g. oxygen 0_2 (0 - 0); a molecule of a compound consists of atoms of different kinds, e.g. water H_20 (H - 0 - H).

MOLLUSC One of a group (or phylum) of invertebrates with a soft, unsegmented body and often a shell.

Examples. Snail, slug, octopus, mussel.

Garden snail

MOON The natural satellite which revolves round the Earth. Its diameter is 3 476km (2 159 miles) and its distance from the Earth is about 384 000km (238 000 miles). The gravity of the Moon, together with that of the Sun, causes the tides in the Earth's oceans and seas.

The Moon and the Earth drawn to scale

MOSS A kind of plant which has a stalk and leaves but no proper roots. Mosses reproduce by spores, and often grow in large groups on trees or rocks.

MOTOR A device or machine for producing kinetic energy from another kind of energy.

Examples. Electric motor (electrical energy).
Clockwork motor (strain energy).

MUSCLE (pr. muss-l) An animal tissue made of bundles of fibre which can contract or relax to cause movement of organs, limbs, etc.

(Do not confuse with mussel which is a kind of mollusc.)

MYRIAPOD (pr. mirr-ee-a-pod) A kind of arthropod with a long segmented body and many legs.

Examples. Centipede (each segment has one pair of legs).
Millipede (each segment has two pairs of legs).

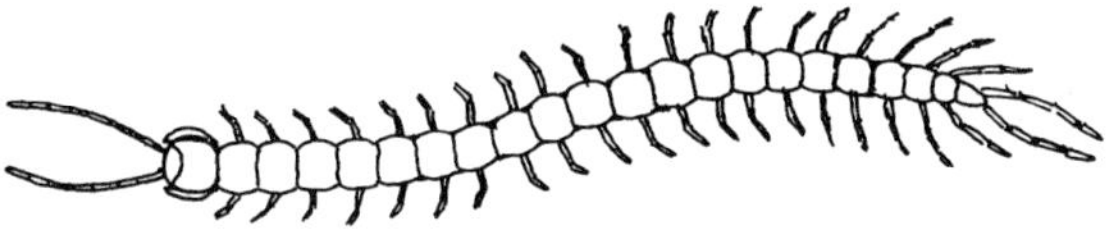

Centipede

NAND CIRCUIT A logic circuit in which the output is high only when the inputs are not all high.

Simplified circuit symbol 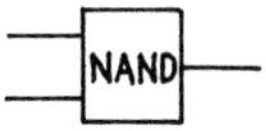

The truth table for a NAND circuit with two inputs is

INPUTS		OUTPUT
0	0	1
0	1	1
1	0	1
1	1	0

NEGATIVE CHARGE A substance, object or piece of material has a negative charge when it contains more than its normal number of electrons.

NERVE An animal tissue made of bundles of fibres (parts of nerve cells) which carry impulses (or signals) from the brain or spinal cord to other parts of the body.

NEUTRAL A substance is neutral if it is neither an acid nor an alkali. A neutral substance has a pH of 7.

Examples. Pure water is a neutral substance.

Sodium chloride (common salt) solution is a neutral substance.

NEUTRALISATION Adding acid to alkali, or alkali to acid, to produce a solution which is neutral (neither acid nor alkali).

Example.

sulphuric acid +	sodium hydroxide	→	sodium sulphate + water
(acid)	(alkali)		(neutral)

NEWTON A unit of force. The force which makes a mass of 1kg accelerate at a rate of 1 metre per second per second. Named after the English scientist Sir Isaac Newton (born 1643, died 1727).

On Earth, a mass of 1 kilogram has a weight of about 10 newtons.

The symbol for newtons is N.

NITRATE A salt formed when nitric acid is neutralised by a base or alkali. Nitrates in the soil are used by plants for producing proteins.

Example. Sodium nitrate (a compound of sodium, nitrogen and oxygen).

NITROGEN An element. A gas (non-metal) without colour or smell. It forms about 78% of the air. Nitrogen is an essential part of the living world because it is one of the elements in nitrates, proteins and DNA. The symbol for nitrogen is N.

NOBLE GAS See INERT GAS.

NON-METAL An element which is not a metal. A non-metal can be a solid (e.g. sulphur), a liquid (e.g. bromine) or a gas (e.g. nitrogen) at normal temperatures.

Non-metals are usually poor conductors of thermal (heat) energy and electricity (except graphite, a form of carbon, which conducts them well), and form acidic oxides. Solid non-metals are often brittle and dull-looking.

NOR CIRCUIT A logic circuit in which the output is high only if all the inputs are low.

Simplified circuit symbol 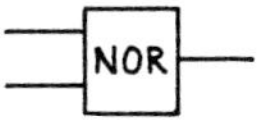

The truth table for a NOR circuit with two inputs is

INPUTS		OUTPUT
0	0	1
0	1	0
1	0	0
1	1	0

NOT CIRCUIT A logic circuit in which the output is high if the input is low, and vice versa. Also called an inverter.

Simplified circuit symbol 

The truth table for a NOT circuit is

INPUT	OUTPUT
0	1
1	0

NUCLEAR REACTION A reaction which changes the nucleus of an atom by (a) the releasing of particles from the nucleus (see RADIOACTIVITY), or (b) the bombardment of the nucleus by particles from outside the nucleus, or (c) nuclear fission (the splitting apart of the nucleus of a large atom, such as uranium, to form smaller nuclei), or (d) nuclear fusion (the joining together of two or more nuclei of small atoms, such as hydrogen, to form a larger nucleus).
Nuclear reactions produce thermal (heat) energy which can be used to operate nuclear power stations, etc.

NUCLEUS <u>In a cell</u> The part of a cell, surrounded by the nuclear membrane, which controls the reactions in the cell.

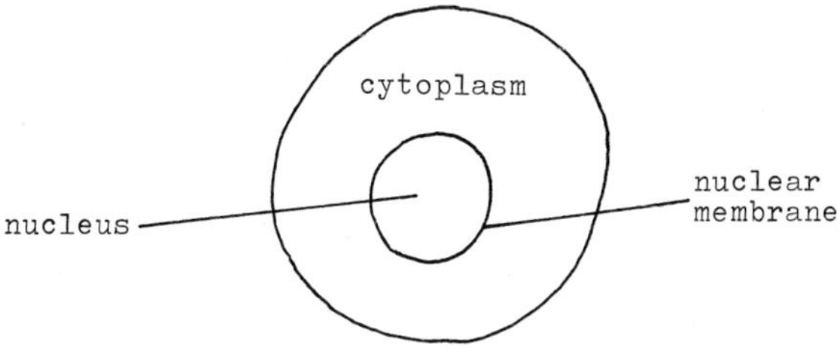

P.T.O. ⇨

In an atom The central part of an atom which contains most of the atom's mass. It is usually made up of protons and neutrons. When a nuclear reaction takes place, the structure of the nucleus is changed.

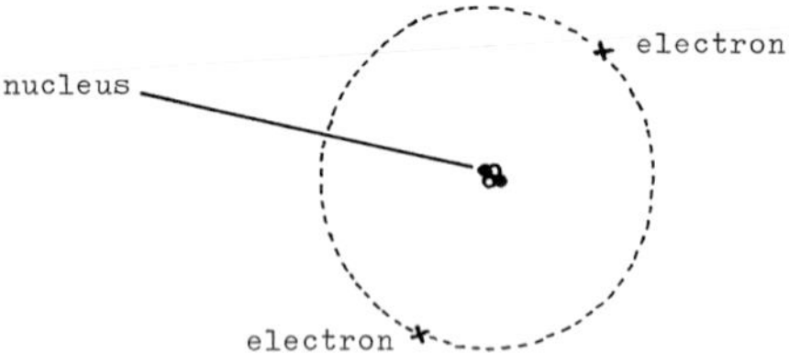

(Helium atom, not drawn to scale)

NUTRIENT A substance, e.g. food, vitamins, mineral salts, etc., which is needed for the life and growth of an organism (animal, plant, etc.).

NUTRITION The process by which organisms take in nutrients (food, etc.) and convert them to different chemicals for production of energy, renewal of tissue, etc.

NYMPH (pr. nimf) The larva of certain insects, such as the dragonfly, mayfly, grasshopper, etc.

OESOPHAGUS (pr. eess-off-a-gus) The part of the gut between the mouth and the stomach.

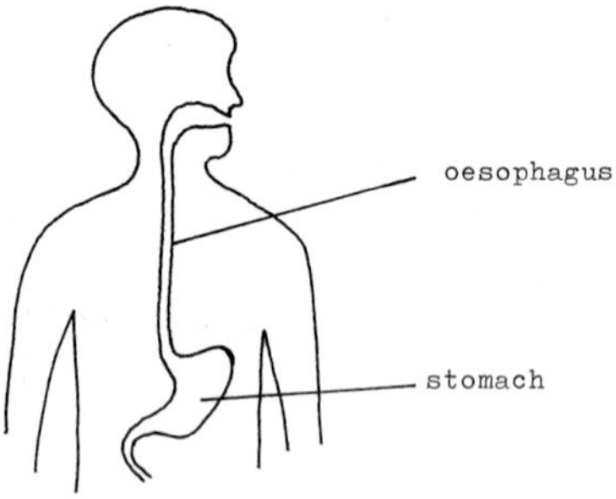

OHM The normal unit of electrical resistance. Named after the German scientist Georg Ohm (born 1787, died 1854). The symbol for ohms is Ω.

OIL A name given to several different substances, all of which are liquid at normal temperatures. Oils are either mineral oils or organic oils.

Mineral oils are hydrocarbons usually obtained from crude oil (in an oil well).

Examples. Diesel oil, paraffin.

Organic oils are compounds of carbon, hydrogen and oxygen produced by plants or animals.

Examples. Olive oil (from the fruits of olive trees), linseed oil (from the seeds of flax plants), fish oil (from sardines, herrings, etc.).

OMNIVORE An animal which eats both animal and plant food.

Examples. Human being, badger.

ORBIT The path or track of a heavenly body (object in space) round another heavenly body.

Example. The orbit of the Earth round the Sun.

OR CIRCUIT A logic circuit in which the output is high if at least one of the inputs is high.

Simplified circuit symbol 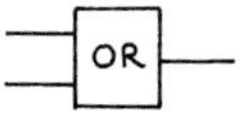

The truth table for an OR circuit with two inputs is

INPUTS		OUTPUT
0	0	0
0	1	1
1	0	1
1	1	1

ORDER A division of a class. See CLASSIFICATION.

ORE A metal (or sometimes a non-metal) compound found in the earth and used for making the metal (or non-metal). Making a metal from an ore is called extracting the metal.

Examples.Bauxite (aluminium oxide) is an ore used for making aluminium.

Haematite (iron oxide) is an ore used for making iron.

ORGAN A part of an organism which does a special job.

Example. Some of the organs in a human body.

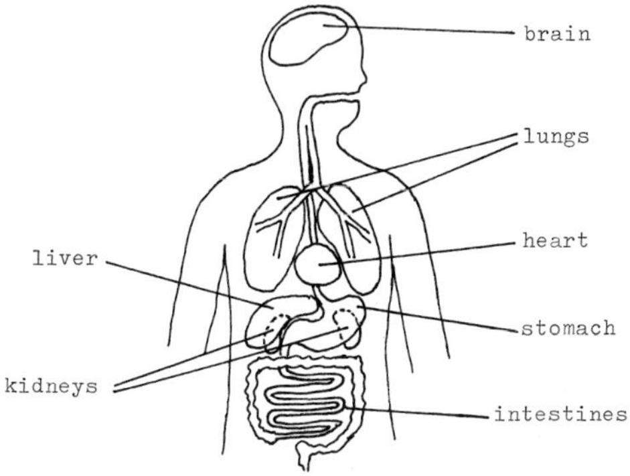

ORGANIC Organic substances are compounds of carbon, many of which are found in nature (including hydrocarbons, carbohydrates, fats, oils and others) but some of which are man-made (including plastics and others).

Organic farming is farming without man-made chemicals, and using only organisms and natural organic substances.

ORGANISM A thing which is capable of living, such as an animal, plant, fungus, bacterium, etc.

OVARY In a female animal, a reproductive organ in which eggs are produced. Most female vertebrates have two ovaries. See UTERUS.

In a flower, the part which contains one or more ovules and in which fertilisation takes place. After fertilisation, an ovary becomes a fruit.

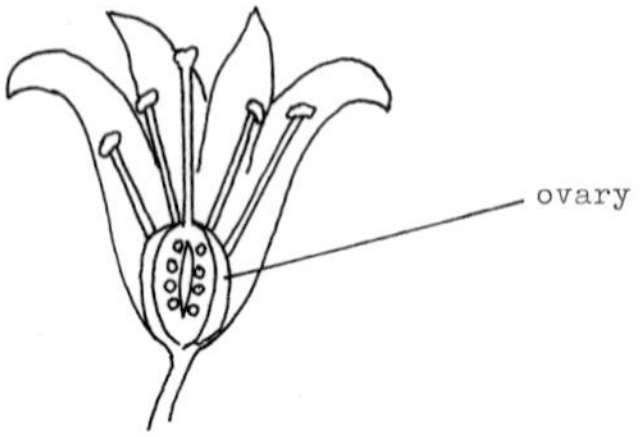

(Bluebell)

OVIDUCT One of the two tubes in the reproductive organs of a mammal which connect the ovaries to the uterus. See UTERUS.

OVULATION (pr. ov-yoo-lay-shn) The releasing of an egg (ovum) from the ovary of a female animal.

OVULE (pr. ov-yool) The small part of a flower which contains the female gamete. In most flowering plants, the ovules are inside the ovary. After fertilisation, the ovule becomes a seed.

OXIDE A compound of oxygen and one other element.

Examples. Copper oxide (copper + oxygen).
Carbon dioxide (carbon + oxygen).
Water (hydrogen + oxygen).

OXYGEN An element. A gas (non-metal) without colour or smell. It forms about 21% of the air. It supports combustion (i.e. things burn in it) and is necessary for aerobic respiration.
When oxygen combines with one other element, an oxide is formed. The ending -ate in the name of a compound means that oxygen is one of the elements in the compound, e.g. copper sulphate (copper, sulphur and oxygen).

The symbol for oxygen is O.

OZONE A form of oxygen whose molecule consists of three oxygen atoms (not two as in ordinary oxygen). There are small quantities of ozone in normal air and larger quantities in the ozone layer.

OZONE LAYER A layer of the Earth's outer atmosphere (air) containing a high concentration of ozone which absorbs ultra-violet rays from the Sun. Without the ozone layer, the ultra-violet rays would kill some kinds of plants and cause skin diseases in animals.

PARALLEL Side by side in a circuit. When two or more components are connected in parallel, each component carries the full current.

Example.

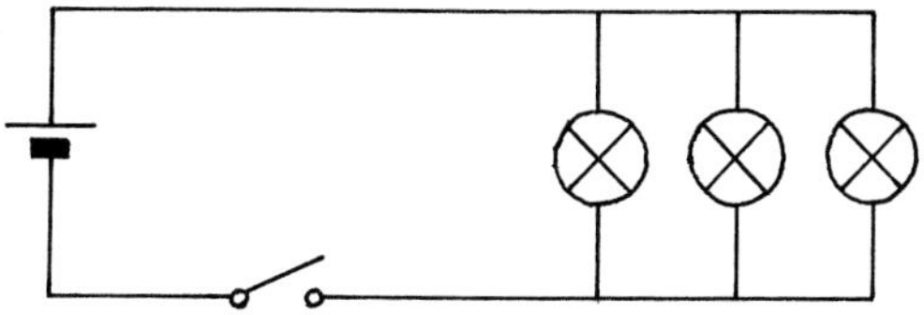

Three lamps connected in parallel. They each have the same brightness as one single lamp because they all use the full current.

PARASITE An organism which lives on (or in), and feeds on, another living organism (called the host), causing harm to the host but not normally killing it.
Examples. Leech, tapeworm, mosquito.

PARTICLE (1) A very small piece of a substance.
(2) One of the small units of matter which make up atoms, including protons, neutrons and electrons.

PD Potential difference. See VOLTAGE.

PENIS (pr. pee-niss) The organ of a male mammal through which (a) urine from the bladder passes out of the body, (b) semen, containing sperms, passes from the testes.

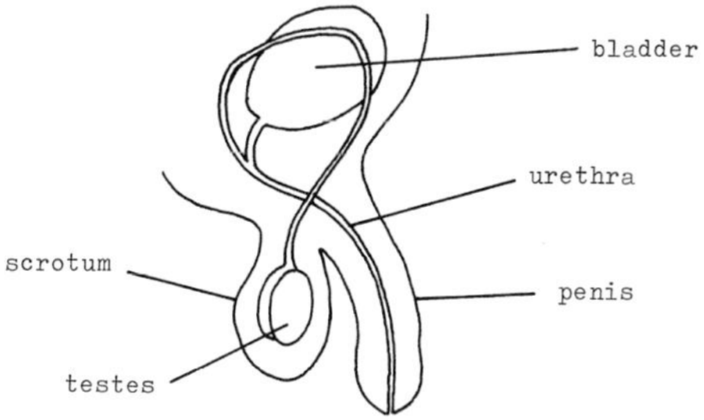

PERIOD Another name for menstruation. See MENSTRUATION.

PETAL One of the parts of a flower which protect the reproductive organs. Petals are often brightly-coloured to attract insects which act as pollinators, carrying pollen from the anther of one flower to the stigma of another.

PHOTOSYNTHESIS (pr. fo-to-sinth-uss-iss) The process by which plants turn carbon dioxide and water into glucose and oxygen by the action of light in the presence of chlorophyll.

pH VALUE A number, from 0 - 14, which shows how acidic or alkaline a solution is. Water (neutral) has a pH of 7. Acids have a pH of less than 7; alkalis have a pH of more than 7. pH values can be measured by testing the solution with an indicator.

pH is short for 'potential of hydrogen' or 'hydrogen ion concentration'.

PHYLUM (pr. fy-lum) A division of a kingdom. The plural is phyla (pr. fy-la). See CLASSIFICATION.

PHYSICS (pr. fizz-ix) The science which deals with mechanics (forces, levers, wheels, machinery, etc.), thermal (heat) energy, light, sound, electricity and the structure and reactions of the nuclei of atoms (nuclear physics). Physics is the study of the properties of all these things (what they are like) and the energy exchanges between them.

A person who studies physics is a physicist (pr. fizz-i-sist).

PIPECLAY TRIANGLE A triangle of wire covered with white pipeclay tubing. Used for holding crucibles.

PITCH A measure of how high or low a note is. Pitch depends on frequency: the higher the frequency of a vibration (of a string, or column of air, etc.), the higher the pitch of the note.

PITFALL TRAP A device for collecting very small animals which live at ground level. It consists of a container (e.g. jam jar) sunk into the ground so that its top is level with the surface. A cover, to keep out rain or predators, can be made with a tile supported on small stones. The animals fall into the jar and are unable to escape.

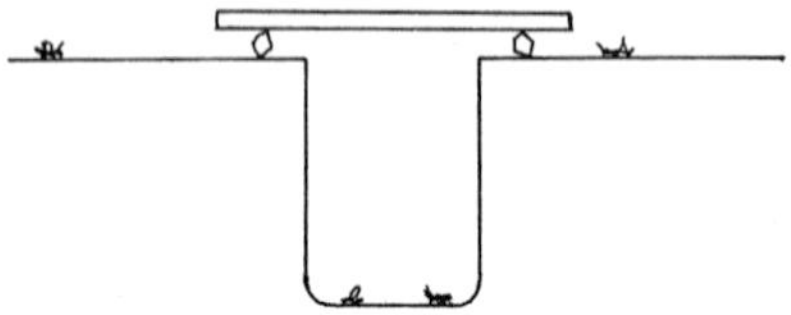

PLACENTA (pr. pla-sent-a) An organ which forms on the wall of the uterus during pregnancy. It transfers oxygen and food from the mother's blood to the embryo's blood, and transfers carbon dioxide and waste products from the embryo's blood to the mother's blood.

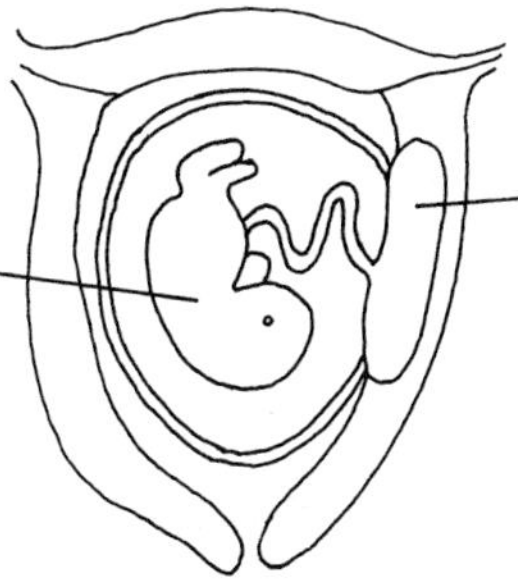

PLANET A heavenly body (object in space) which revolves round the Sun in an elliptical orbit, and shines by reflecting light from the Sun.

Names of the eight planets, from nearest Sun to furthest, are Mercury, Venus, Earth, Mars, Jupiter, Saturn, Uranus (pr. yoor-un-us), Neptune.

(Pluto, once known as the ninth planet, is no longer included in the list of proper planets.)

The order of the planets can be remembered by Many Very Elderly Men Just Sit Under Newspapers.

PLANKTON Tiny plant or animal organisms, sometimes of only one cell, which drift on the surfaces of seas and lakes.

PLANT An organism which normally (a) has cells with cell walls; (b) cannot move of its own accord; (c) has no sense organs; (d) makes its own food from simple chemicals, such as carbon dioxide, mineral salts, etc.

PLASMA The yellow liquid part of blood which contains dissolved chemicals such as proteins, glucose, urea, etc.

PLASTIC A kind of man-made (synthetic) organic substance which can be moulded to a chosen shape and then set solid.

Example. PVC (polyvinyl chloride).

PLATELETS Small cell fragments which occur in blood and which harden (or clot) the blood to stop wounds bleeding.

POLE One of the two ends of a magnet where the strongest magnetic effects occur. One pole is the north-seeking (or north) pole, and the other is the south-seeking (or south) pole.

When two magnets are placed close together, unlike (different) poles attract one another, and like (similar) poles repel one another (push one another away).

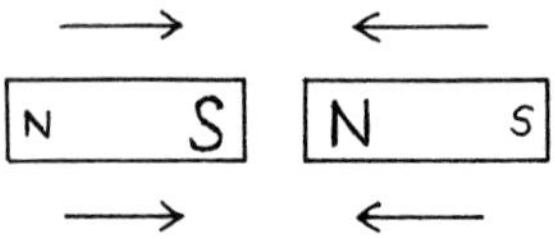

Unlike poles together
(attraction)

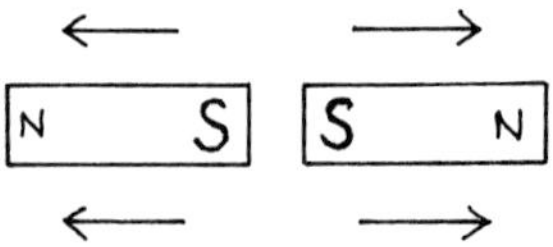

Like poles together
(repulsion)

POLLEN A collection of tiny grains produced in the anthers of a flower, and containing male gametes (reproductive cells).

POLLINATION The process in which pollen is transferred from the anther of a flower to the stigma of the same or another flower. This transfer can be made by the wind or by insects which visit the flower.

POLLUTION Introduction, usually by human beings, of harmful chemicals into the natural world, e.g. smoke and acid fumes into the air, oil into the sea, etc.

POPULATION The number of examples of a certain species of organism living in a certain area.
Examples. The number of daisies in a field.
The number of human beings in South America.

POSITIVE CHARGE A substance, object or piece of material has a positive charge when it contains less than its normal number of electrons.

POTASSIUM An element. A (☠ DANGEROUS!) metal, some of whose compounds are used as plant fertilisers.

Potassium permanganate, a purple crystalline salt, decomposes to give oxygen when heated.

The symbol for potassium is K (from its old name kalium).

POTENTIAL DIFFERENCE See VOLTAGE.

POTENTIAL ENERGY The energy which something has by being in a certain position. Also called stored energy.

Example. The energy of a cyclist at the top of a hill.

PRECIPITATE An insoluble substance produced from a solution by a physical change or chemical reaction.

Example. A precipitate of calcium carbonate is formed when carbon dioxide reacts with lime water (the lime water turns 'milky').

PREDATOR (pr. pred-a-ter) An animal which kills and eats another animal. The other animal is the prey of the predator.

Example. A fox is a predator, and its prey may be an animal such as a rabbit or pheasant.

PREGNANT A female is pregnant from the time her egg is fertilised until the time her baby is born. A human female is usually pregnant for about nine months. Being pregnant is called pregnancy.

PRESSURE The force acting over a certain area. Pressure is usually measured in newtons per square metre (N/m^2).

$$\text{Pressure} = \frac{\text{Force}}{\text{Area}}$$

PRIMARY CONSUMER A consumer which eats plant life. A herbivore.

PRISM (1) A solid with both ends exactly the same shape and size, e.g. triangular prism.

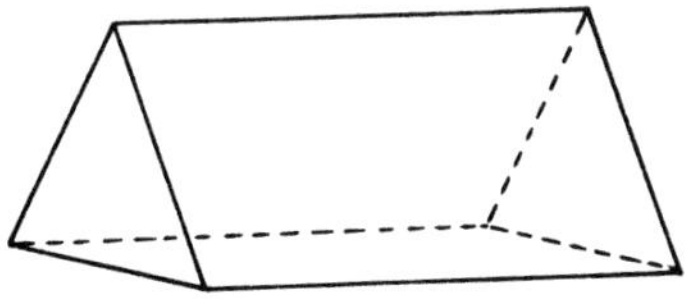

(2) A piece of glass or other transparent substance in the shape of a triangular prism which can split up white light to make a spectrum (colours of the rainbow).

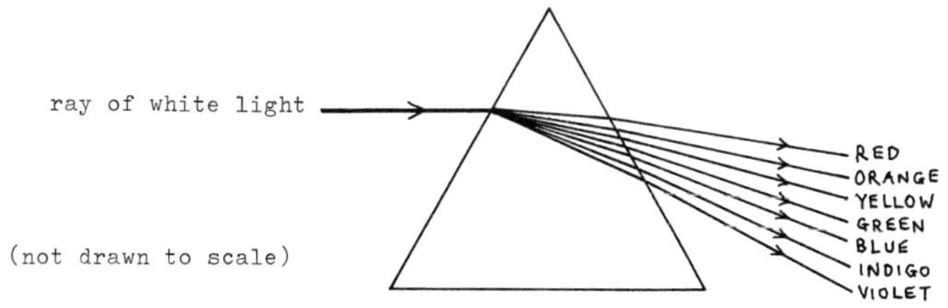

The colours of the spectrum can be remembered by
Run Off, You Girls! Boys In View.

Prisms are often used in optical instruments such as binoculars.

PRODUCER An organism (usually a green plant) which can produce nutrient tissue (food) from simple chemicals, often by photosynthesis.

PROPERTIES Things, or features, which a substance possesses, such as colour, hardness, transparency, acidity, alkalinity, density, conductivity, etc.

PROTEIN A complicated substance made up of organic acids. All proteins contain carbon, hydrogen, nitrogen and oxygen; some also contain other elements.

Proteins are an important part of the human diet as they are essential for normal growth, e.g. as enzymes, or for repairing or renewing damaged tissue, etc. Foods which are rich in protein include fish, lean meat, milk, cheese, peanuts, etc.

PROTOPLASM The living contents of the cells of organisms. Protoplasm consists of proteins and water.

PUBERTY (pr. pyoo-ber-ty) The time during the life of a human being when his or her reproductive organs become larger and are capable, for the first time, of producing sperm or eggs. Puberty usually happens between the ages of about 11 and 15 years. Other physical changes include extra growth of hair, the development of a girl's breasts and the changing or 'breaking' of a boy's voice.

PULLEY A wheel whose rim has a groove round which a string, rope or belt can pass.

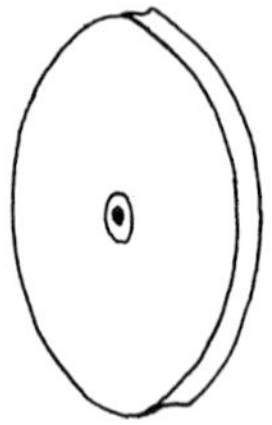

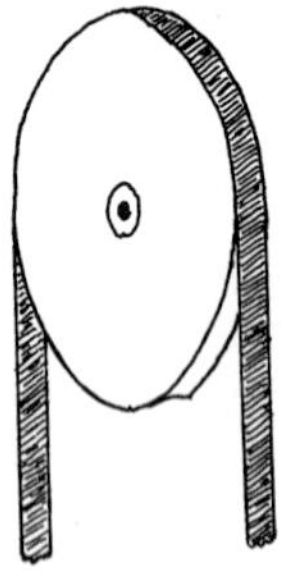

PULSE The increased blood pressure in the arteries at each beat of the heart. The pulse can be felt where an artery crosses a bone, e.g. at the wrist. The pulse (or heartbeat) rate is the number of beats per minute.

PUPA (pr. pyoo-per) An insect at the stage between being a larva and a fully-developed insect. At the pupa stage, the insect does not eat.

Example. Pupa of Garden Tiger Moth.

PUSH SWITCH A switch operated by a button. Pressing the button changes the switch from off to on, or from on to off.

Circuit diagram symbol 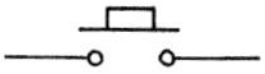

QUADRAT An area of ground (usually 1 square metre), often marked out with a square frame (also called a quadrat), in which all the organisms can be counted or studied.

RADIATION ENERGY The energy generated by the emission (giving off) of rays.

Example. Light energy.

Radiation energy is the only kind of energy which can travel through a vacuum, e.g. the radiation energy from the Sun which travels through space.

RADIOACTIVITY The emission, or releasing, of alpha particles (helium nuclei), beta particles (electrons) or gamma rays, from the nuclei of atoms of certain elements, e.g. uranium.

RAW MATERIAL The substance, or substances, from which something is made or manufactured, either in nature or by human beings.

REACTION (pr. ree-ak-shn) See CHEMICAL REACTION and NUCLEAR REACTION.

REACTIVITY SERIES Also called electrochemical series. A list of metal elements in order of their ability to replace other metals from their salts. A metal higher in the list will react with a salt of a lower metal, producing the lower metal and a salt of the higher one. The higher the metal is in the series, the more reactive it is. A metal lower in the series will not replace a metal higher in the series.

Example.

zinc + copper sulphate → copper + zinc sulphate

As zinc is higher in the series than copper, it will replace copper.

Reactivity Series
(showing some well-known metals)
sodium
magnesium
aluminium
zinc
iron
tin
lead
(hydrogen)
copper
mercury
silver
gold

Hydrogen (a non-metal) is usually included in the series because it forms acids in the same way that metals form salts, and follows the reactivity series.

Example.

zinc + hydrogen chloride → hydrogen + zinc chloride

As zinc is higher in the series than hydrogen, it will replace hydrogen.

RECTIFIER A component which allows the flow of an electric current in only one direction. Usually a diode.

RECYCLE To process a substance so that it can be used again, often in order to conserve the world's natural resources.

Example. Used paper is processed to make recycled paper.

REDUCTION Removing oxygen from a substance, or adding hydrogen to it, in a chemical reaction.

Example.

copper oxide + hydrogen $\xrightarrow{\text{heat}}$ copper + water

The copper oxide has been reduced to copper by hydrogen. Oxygen has been removed from the copper oxide.

REED RELAY A component used for switching a circuit on or off by using another circuit. It is made up of a reed switch surrounded by a coil. When a current is passed through the coil, it acts like a magnet and closes (turns on) the reed switch.

Circuit diagram symbol

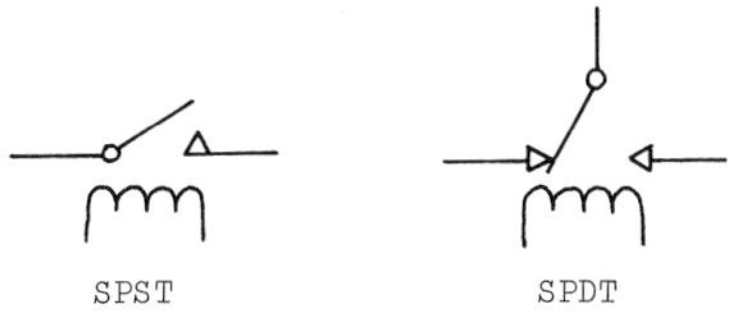

Example. When a current is passed through circuit A, the coil acts as a magnet and closes the reed switch so that current can pass through circuit B.

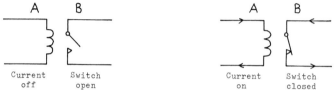

REED SWITCH A switch containing two metal reeds which make contact (switch on) when magnetised.

Circuit diagram symbol

REFLECTION The returning of light or sound from a surface. The best reflection of light is obtained from a shiny surface such as a mirror. Sound reflection creates an echo.

REFRACTION The bending (changing of direction) of a ray of light passing from one medium (substance) to another.

Example. When a ray of light passes from water to air, it is refracted. This explains why a stick appears to bend when it is immersed in water.

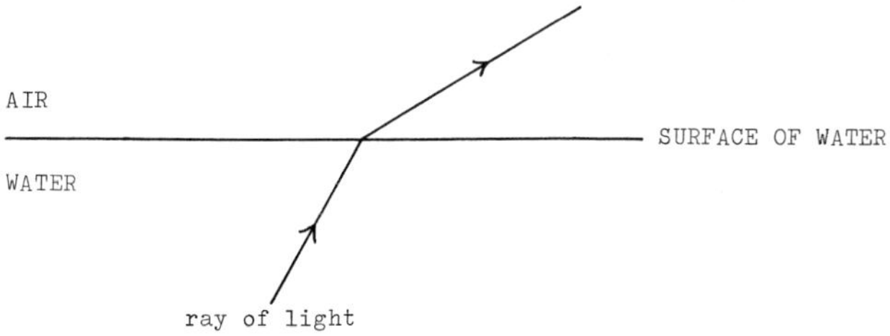

RELAY A device for switching a circuit on or off by using another circuit. See REED RELAY.

REPRODUCTION Making more examples of the same kind of living thing, either sexually or asexually.

Sexual reproduction requires two parents (one male and one female) and occurs when the male and female gametes join together.

Asexual reproduction requires only one parent.

REPTILE One of a class of cold-blooded vertebrate animals. Reptiles have scaly skins and air-breathing lungs, and they lay eggs. Most reptiles are land animals.

Examples. Snakes, lizards, crocodiles, turtles, tortoises.

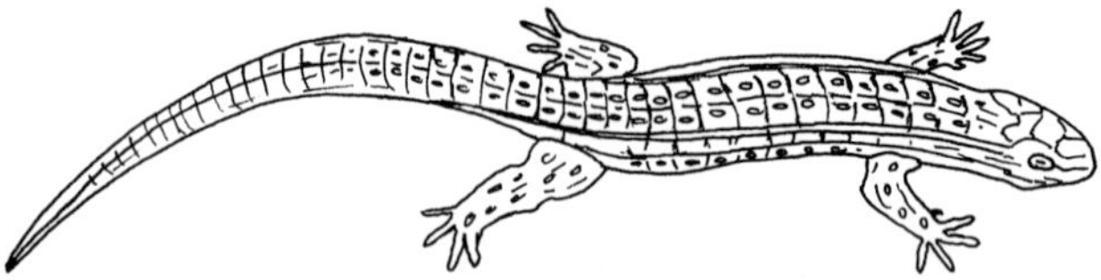

Common lizard

RESISTANCE Anything which prevents or opposes the flow of an electric current.

RESISTOR A component which resists or opposes the flow of an electric current.

Circuit diagram symbols

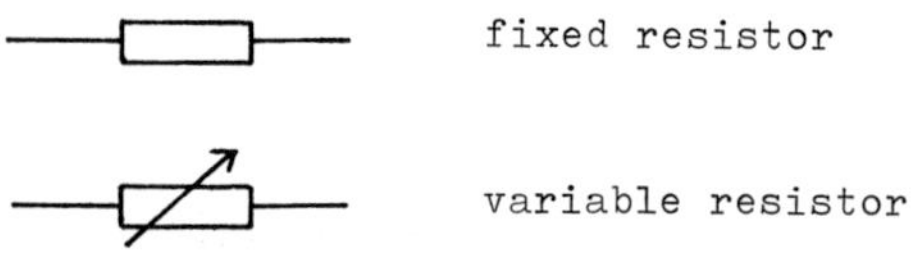

RESPIRATION A chemical reaction in an organism to produce energy.

Aerobic respiration (respiration with oxygen) The process in which oxygen is absorbed into an organism and reacts with carbohydrates to produce energy, carbon dioxide and water.

Example. In human beings and other land vertebrates, air is breathed into the lungs where oxygen is transferred to the blood. The oxygen is then carried to the tissues where respiration takes place.

Anaerobic respiration (respiration without oxygen) The process in which carbohydrates are decomposed by an organism to produce energy, carbon dioxide and a new substance.

Examples. Yeast respires anaerobically during fermentation. It uses sugar which is converted to alcohol, carbon dioxide and energy.

Human muscles respire anaerobically if their supply of oxygen runs out. Sugar is converted to lactic acid and energy (a build-up of lactic acid in muscles can cause cramp).

RHEOSTAT (pr. <u>ree</u>-o-stat) Another name for VARIABLE RESISTOR.

ROCK SALT Sodium chloride in a crude state (containing impurities such as sand), just as it is dug out of the earth. It can be purified to common salt by solution, filtration and evaporation.

ROOT The part of a plant which (a) anchors the plant in the ground; (b) absorbs water and mineral (inorganic) salts such as phosphates, sulphates, calcium salts, etc., from the soil. In some plants, the root also acts as a food store.

RUST An orangey-brown form of hydrated iron oxide produced when iron comes into contact with both air and water.

SALT Any crystalline substance which can be made by neutralising an acid with a base (or vice versa).

Some common kinds of salt are carbonates, chlorides, nitrates and sulphates.

Salt used for flavouring food is normally common salt (sodium chloride).

SAPROPHYTE (pr. <u>sap</u>-ro-fyt) An organism which lives on (or in), and feeds on, a dead plant, animal, etc.

Example. A fungus growing on a dead tree.

SATELLITE A heavenly body (an object in space) which revolves round a planet and shines by reflecting light from the Sun. The Earth's natural satellite is the Moon. The other planets which have natural satellites are Mars (2 satellites), Jupiter (at least 63), Saturn (at least 56), Uranus (at least 27), Neptune (at least 13).

There are also many man-made satellites revolving round the Earth. These have been launched from the Earth and are used for various purposes, such as weather forecasting, communications (telephone and television), etc.

SCROTUM The sac which contains the testes. See PENIS.

SECONDARY CONSUMER A consumer which eats a primary consumer.

SEED A fertilised ovule consisting of a plant embryo and its food store surrounded by a thick seed coat for protection from damage, insects, dehydration, etc.

SEGMENTED A segmented organism, or part of an organism, is one that is made up of distinct separate sections called segments.

Example. The abdomen of an earwig is segmented.

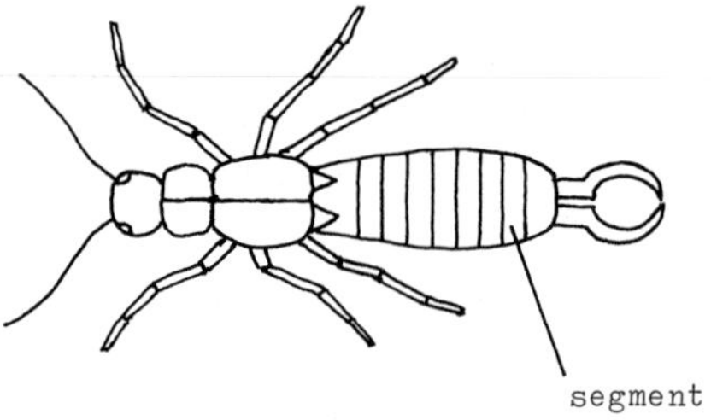

SEMEN (pr. see-mn) The white liquid containing sperms which is produced in the reproductive organs of a male mammal.

SEPAL (pr. sep-l) One of the (usually green) parts of a flower which protect the bud.

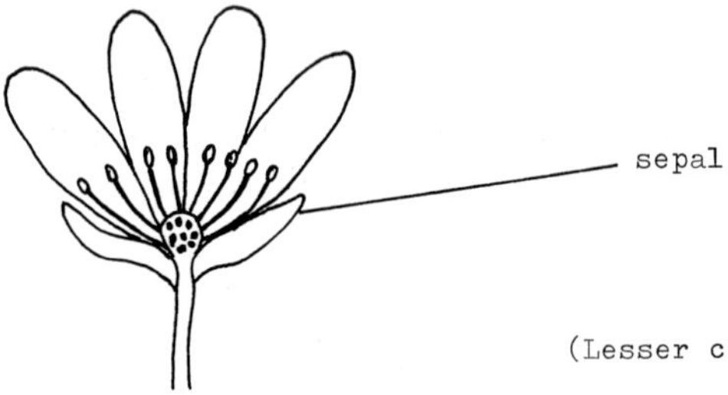

SERIES One after another in a circuit. When two or more components are connected in series they share the current.

Example.

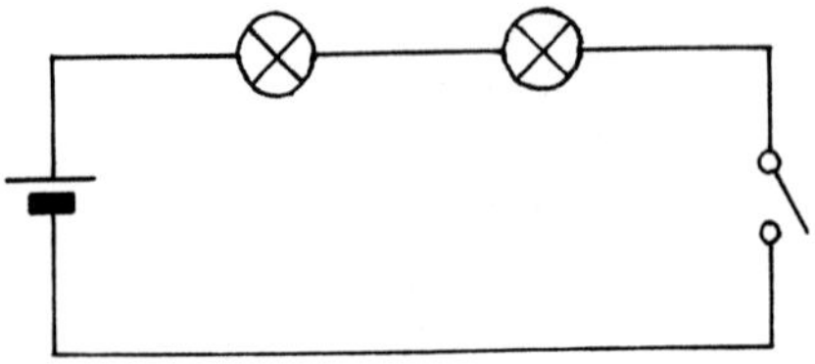

Two lamps connected in series.

They would be dimmer than one single lamp because they share the current.

SEXUAL INTERCOURSE The process in which the penis of a male human being (or other mammal) is inserted into the vagina of a female. Sexual intercourse sometimes results in a sperm from the male fertilising the egg in the female.

SEXUAL REPRODUCTION Making more examples of the same species of animal or plant by the joining together of a male and female gamete.

SHORT CIRCUIT A conductor placed across a circuit so that the current takes a 'short cut' (finds an easier way with less resistance) through the conductor.

SILVER An element. A soft, shiny white metal. Used for silver plating (coating items such as sports cups, etc., with silver) and for making jewellery, mirrors, etc. Silver salts are used to make films and printing paper for photography.

The symbol for silver is Ag (from its old name argentum).

SINGLE-POLE SWITCH A switch with only one moving contact.

<u>Single-pole single-throw (SPST) switch</u> An ordinary on/off switch.

Circuit diagram symbol

<u>Single-pole double-throw (SPDT) switch</u> A switch whose single moving contact can close (turn on) one of two different circuits. When the switch is activated, one circuit is turned on while the other is turned off.

Circuit diagram symbol

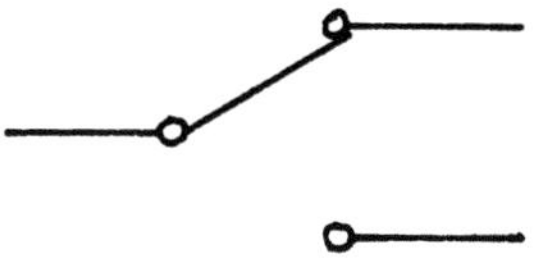

Example. Two SPDT switches can operate a stair light which can be turned on or off from either the top or bottom of the stairs.

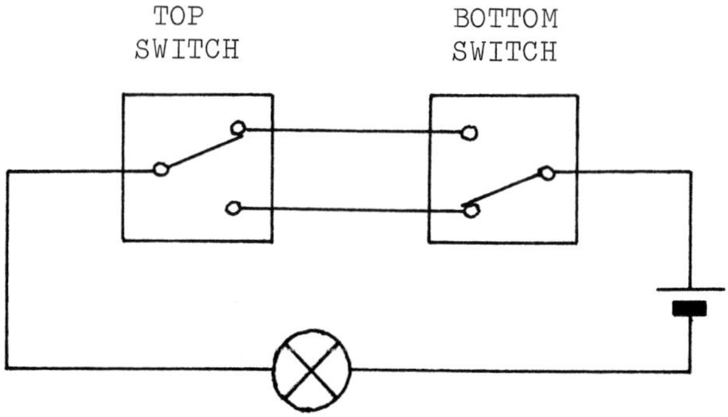

The diagram shows one of the two possible OFF positions. By throwing (switching) either switch, the light will go on.

SKELETON The hard supporting framework of an animal. An animal with an endoskeleton has its skeleton, made mainly of bones, inside it, e.g. human being. An animal with an exoskeleton has its skeleton on the outside for protection, e.g. crab.

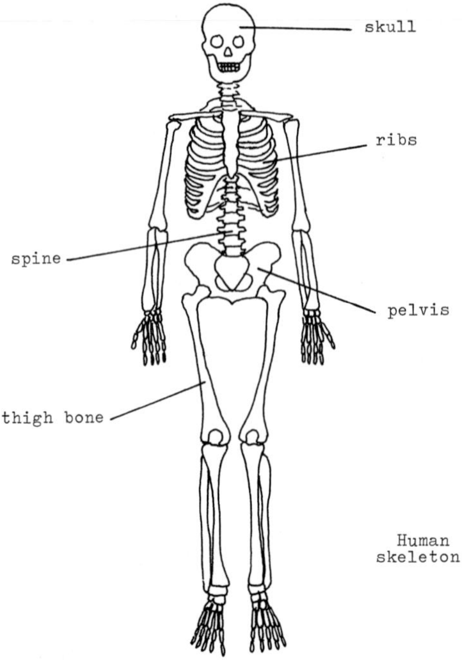

Human skeleton

SODIUM An element. A light silvery-grey metal which burns with a yellow flame and reacts violently with water.

(☠ DANGEROUS SUBSTANCE. NEVER TOUCH SODIUM AND NEVER EXPERIMENT WITH IT - LIKELY TO CATCH FIRE, EXPLODE AND CAUSE SEVERE BURNS OR OTHER INJURIES.)
Sodium is used in sodium vapour street lighting. Its compounds include caustic soda (sodium hydroxide), common salt (sodium chloride), bicarbonate of soda (sodium hydrogen carbonate), etc.

SODIUM CHLORIDE The chemical name for rock salt and common salt (salt used for flavouring food).

SOIL A mixture of particles of rock, partly decomposed organisms (humus), water (which contains mineral salts) and air.

SOLAR SYSTEM The group of heavenly bodies (objects in space) which includes the Sun and its planets (and their satellites). See PLANET and SATELLITE.

SOLID A substance which is too cold to be a liquid or a gas. A substance is a solid when its temperature is below its freezing point.

When a solid is poured or tipped into a container, it keeps its original shape, unlike a liquid or gas.

The molecules of a solid can vibrate from side to side but stay in the same positions.

SOLUBLE A substance is soluble in a liquid if it dissolves in the liquid (to make a solution).

Example. Copper sulphate dissolves in water, so copper sulphate is soluble in water.

SOLUTE (pr. <u>sol</u>-yoot) The substance which is dissolved in a liquid to make a solution.

Example. When sugar is dissolved in water, the solute is sugar.

SOLUTION A liquid consisting of a solvent in which one or more substances (solutes) have dissolved.

Example. A solution of salt in water.

A <u>saturated solution</u> is a solution which contains the largest possible amount of the dissolved substance, i.e. a solution in which no more of the substance will dissolve.

SOLVENT The liquid in which a substance is dissolved to make a solution.

Example. When sugar is dissolved in water, the solvent is water.

SOUND A wave movement, caused by vibration, which can be heard. A kind of energy.

Sound travels (at ordinary temperatures) at about 340 metres per second or about 760 miles per hour ($^1/_5$ mile per second).

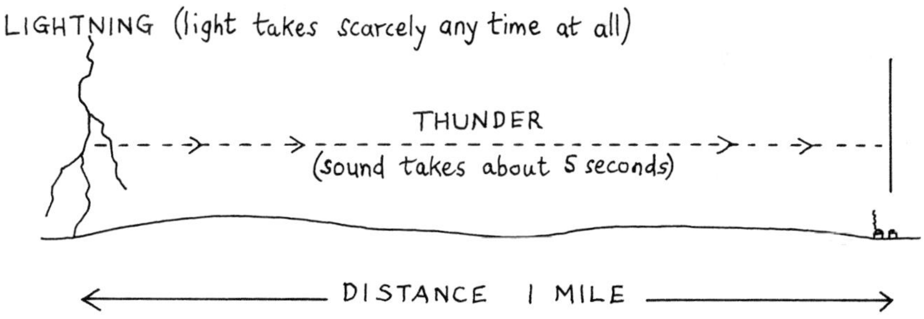

To find how far away a thunderstorm is, count the seconds from the flash of lightning to the sound of thunder. Every 5 seconds mean a distance of about 1 mile (1.61km).

SPATULA (pr. spat-yoo-la) A long, flat, spoonlike implement, made from metal or plastic, and used for transferring solid substances from one container to another.

SPDT SWITCH Single-pole double-throw switch. See SINGLE-POLE SWITCH.

SPECIES (pr. spee-sheez) A division of a genus. See CLASSIFICATION. Each different sort of living thing is a separate species. Organisms which reproduce sexually can normally do this only with members of the same species.

Each identified species is given a scientific Latin name made up of two words (and written either in italics or underlined). The first word is the genus to which the living thing belongs; the second word is the species. Scientists all over the world, whatever their own language, can understand what the Latin names mean.

Examples. *Bellis perennis* is the scientific name for a daisy.

Hirundo rustica is the scientific name for a swallow.

SPECIMEN An example of a substance, animal, plant, etc., especially one which is used for scientific investigation.

SPECTRUM The band of colours produced when light is split up by a prism, or by water droplets in a rainbow. See PRISM.

SPERM A male gamete, or reproductive cell of an animal.

Human sperm (1500X real length)

SPIDER A kind of arachnid which has a spinneret for making webs. A spider uses its web to trap the insects on which it feeds.

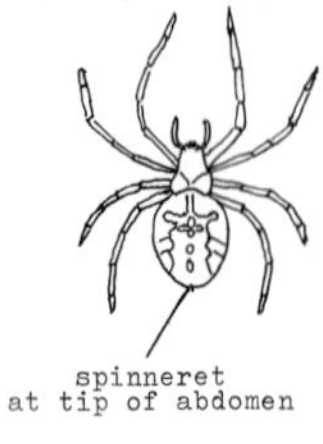

Garden spider

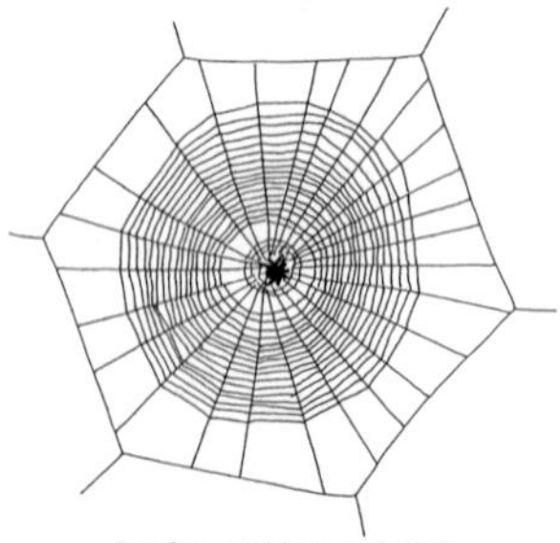

Garden spider and web

SPINAL CORD A hollow tube, in vertebrates, extending from the brain to the end of the spine and protected by the bones of the spine. It carries nerve impulses (signals) from one part of the body to another, and from the brain to the body and the body to the brain.

SPINE The backbone, vertebral column or spinal column of an animal. See SKELETON.

SPORE A tiny unit, often of only one cell, produced by fungi and some other organisms, such as mosses and ferns, during reproduction.

SPRING BALANCE A device for finding the weight of an object (usually in newtons). The object is hung on a spring which stretches to show the weight on a scale.

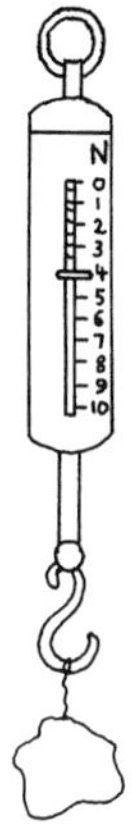

SPST SWITCH Single-pole single-throw switch. See SINGLE-POLE SWITCH.

STALK Another word for STEM.

STAMEN The male reproductive organ in a flower. It consists of a stem (called a filament) and an anther (tip). Pollen is produced in the anther.

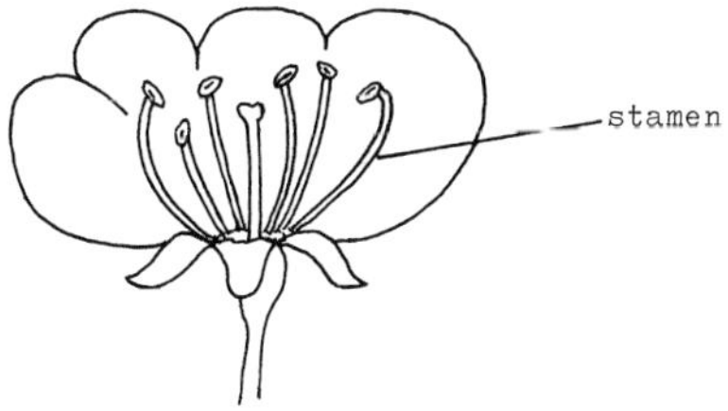

(Hawthorn)

STAR A heavenly body (an object in space) which produces its own light and thermal (heat) energy by nuclear reactions.

The nearest star to us is the Sun. Its distance from us is about 1.5×10^8 km (150 000 000km) or 9.3×10^7 miles (93 000 000 miles).

The next nearest star is Proxima Centauri. Its distance is about 4×10^{13} km (40 000 000 000 000km) or 2.5×10^{13} miles (25 000 000 000 000 miles) or 4.3 light years.

STARCH A white insoluble carbohydrate formed from glucose and used by plants for storage of energy. Potatoes and some kinds of grain crops are important sources of starch.

Starch can be easily detected by testing with iodine solution which turns from brown to very dark blue.

STATES OF MATTER The three states of matter are solid, liquid and gas.

A solid has a definite volume and a definite shape. Its molecules vibrate but stay in the same positions.

A liquid has a definite volume but not a definite shape. It will adopt the shape of a container into which it is put, sinking down as far as it can and forming a flat top (surface). Its molecules are free to move about in a restricted way.

A gas has neither a definite volume nor a definite shape. It will spread out (diffuse) to fill the container into which it is put. Its molecules are free to move about at high speeds.

A solid can usually be turned into a liquid, or a liquid into a gas, by heating.

A gas can usually be turned into a liquid, or a liquid into a solid, by cooling.

STATIC ELECTRICITY A stationary (staying still) charge possessed by an object.

Example. The plastic tube of a fountain pen or ball pen, when rubbed against cloth, can become charged with static electricity and will pick up small pieces of paper.

STEAM The invisible gas formed when water boils. Steam is water which is above its boiling point and in the form of a gas. The 'gap' between the spout of a kettle of boiling water and the water droplets (condensation) is steam.

STEEL An alloy made mainly of iron but containing a small amount of carbon, and sometimes other elements. There are many different kinds of steel, depending on which other elements it contains, and these different kinds all have special uses.

Examples. Ordinary carbon steel is used for girders (for building), pipes and tubes, car bodies, etc. Tungsten steel is used for making tools, saw blades, etc. Stainless steel (containing chromium) is used for making cutlery (knives, forks, spoons, etc.).

STEM The thin tubular central part of a plant, usually above the ground, which bears the buds, flowers and leaves, and carries water and nutrients to all parts of the plant.

A stem can also be the thin part of a section of a plant, such as the stem of a stamen.

STIGMA The sticky tip of the female part of a flower. The stigma collects pollen for fertilisation.

STOMACH The large part of the gut below the oesophagus in which food is stored and partly digested. See GUT.

STOPWATCH A watch which can be stopped, set back to zero, and started again. Used for timing experiments, sports events, etc.

STRAIN ENERGY The energy stored by an object or a substance by stretching it or compressing (squashing) it.

Example. When a spring is stretched, the energy transferred to it by stretching is stored in the spring as strain energy. If the spring is allowed to return to its original shape, the energy is released.

Strain energy can be used for operating clockwork motors, for firing arrows from bows, for compressed air drills, etc.

STYLE The stem of the female part of a flower, joining the stigma to the ovary.

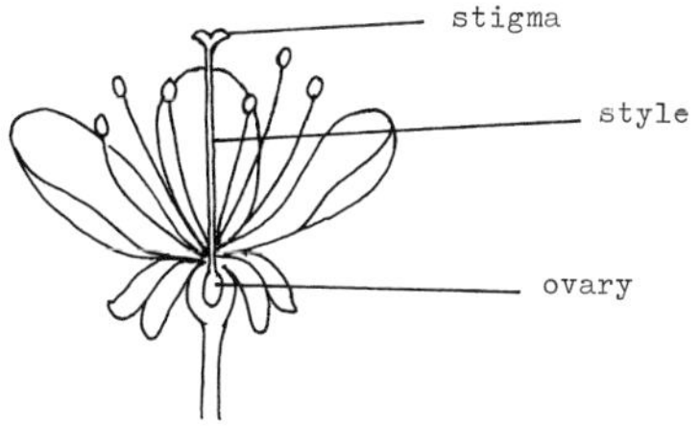

(Plum blossom)

SUBSTANCE A chemical (either an element, a compound or a mixture). A substance can be in the form of a solid, liquid or gas.

SUGAR One of a group of sweet-tasting carbohydrates which includes 'ordinary' sugar (sucrose), glucose, fructose and others.

SULPHUR An element. A solid, usually yellow, non-metal, which burns with a blue flame to produce choking fumes of sulphur dioxide and sulphur trioxide. Sulphur is one of the elements in sulphuric acid and sulpha drugs (and bad eggs and stink bombs).
The symbol for sulphur is S.

SULPHUR DIOXIDE A choking, acidic, colourless gas formed when sulphur is burned in air. It dissolves in water to form sulphurous acid. Sulphur dioxide released into the air from factories is a pollutant and can cause poor air quality and acid rain.

SUN The star which is the centre of the solar system and round which the planets (including Earth) revolve in elliptical orbits. It is made of gas– mostly hydrogen which is being converted into helium by nuclear reactions.

The Sun provides light and thermal (heat) energy which are essential for life on Earth. The energy from the Sun also creates changes in climate and weather, and is therefore the source of natural water power and wind power. The Sun's energy is stored in plants, including those which lived millions of years ago and are now used as fossil fuels.

The Sun is about 1.5×10^8 km (150 000 000km) or 9.3×10^7 miles (93 000 000 miles) from Earth and its diameter is about 1.39×10^6 km (1 390 000km) or 8.6×10^5 miles (860 000 miles).

SUSPENSION A liquid or gas which has particles of a solid or liquid spread throughout it.

A suspension of a liquid in a liquid is also called an emulsion.
If a suspension of a solid in a liquid is filtered, the solid is unable to pass through the paper and is left behind.

Examples. Lime water which has become 'milky' (solid in liquid). Oil shaken up with water (liquid in liquid). Smoke (solid in gas). Mist (liquid in gas).

SWITCH A component which, when OFF, breaks (leaves a gap in) an electric circuit to prevent the flow of current, or, when ON, completes the circuit (joins the gap) to allow the flow of current.

Circuit diagram symbol for simple on/off (SPST) switch. 

See also PUSH SWITCH, REED SWITCH and SINGLE-POLE SWITCH.

SYMBIOSIS (pr. sim-by-oh-sis) A relationship between two organisms in which each organism depends on the other and benefits from the other.

Example. The relationship between an alga and a fungus in a lichen is a symbiosis.

SYMBOL (pr. sim-bl) (1) A short way of writing the name of an element, or one atom of an element.

Examples. H for hydrogen, Zn for zinc.

For a list of common elements and their symbols, see ELEMENT.

(2) A simple drawing to represent a component in an electrical circuit.

Example. 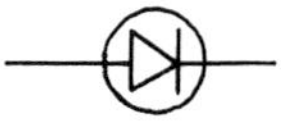 is the symbol for a diode.

For a list of circuit symbols, see CIRCUIT SYMBOLS.

SYRINGE (pr. si-rinj) A piece of apparatus made of a piston which moves up and down a cylinder. It is used for collecting and releasing liquids or gases.

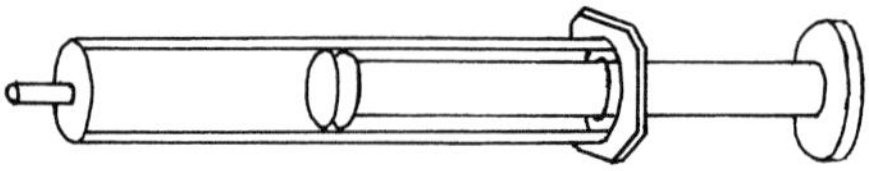

TELESCOPE A device for magnifying distant objects, thus making them appear nearer.
Astronomical telescopes are for observing the night sky (galaxies, stars, planets, etc.). There are two main kinds of astronomical telescope: the refractor, consisting basically of two lenses (an object glass and an eyepiece); the reflector, usually consisting of two mirrors and an eyepiece lens.

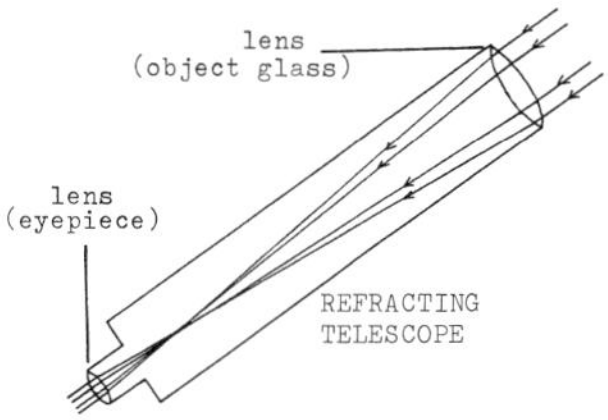

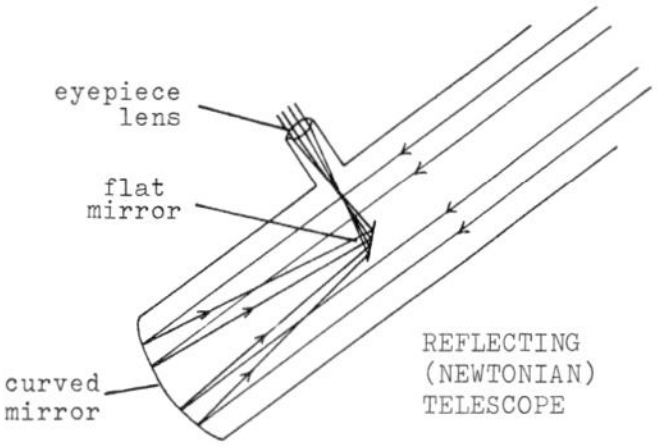

Terrestrial telescopes are normally refractors, but they have an extra lens which turns the image (which is upside down in an astronomical refractor) the right way up, making it suitable for normal use, such as bird watching, etc.
Radiotelescopes are telescopes which pick up radio signals from outer space. Some radiotelescopes are shaped like giant satellite dishes, and others consist of long lines of aerials spread out in various patterns. The signals picked up by radiotelescopes give us information about stars and galaxies which cannot be obtained with ordinary (optical) telescopes.

TEMPERATURE A measurement of hotness or coldness. The usual scientific temperature scale is the Celsius scale. The instrument normally used for measuring temperature is a thermometer.

TERRESTRIAL Living or growing on land.
Example. A rabbit is a terrestrial mammal.

TERTIARY CONSUMER A consumer which eats a secondary consumer.

TESTES (pr. tess-teez) The two glands in a male human, or other mammal, which produce sperms. The testes (each one is a testis) are held in a sac, called the scrotum, behind the penis. Testes are also called testicles. See PENIS.

TEST TUBE A tube made of heat-resistant glass and sealed at one end. Used for heating chemicals, testing solutions, etc.

Usually drawn

THERMAL ENERGY The energy gained by a substance or object when it is heated.
All molecules move. Those in gases move freely at great speeds, those in liquids move freely but more slowly, and those in solids vibrate from side to side but stay in the same positions. If a substance or an object is heated, the energy it gains causes its molecules to move faster, which can sometimes result in melting or evaporation. Because the molecules are moving faster they are said to have gained thermal energy.
Thermal energy is also called internal energy (and sometimes heat energy).

THERMOMETER (pr. ther-mom-it-er) An instrument for measuring temperature. The scale of a thermometer is usually marked in degrees Celsius (°C).

THISTLE FUNNEL A funnel with a long stem and a top shaped like a thistle flower. It is often used for pouring a liquid on to a solid in a flask or bottle for the production of gas. The long stem is adjusted so that it stays under the liquid and prevents (most of) the gas from escaping up the funnel.

Thistle funnel

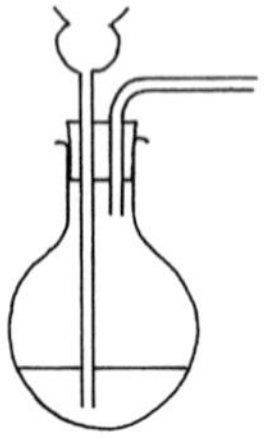

Thistle funnel used for production of gas

THORAX The part of the body of an animal between its head and its abdomen. In a vertebrate, the thorax contains the heart and lungs. In an insect, the legs and wings normally grow from the thorax.

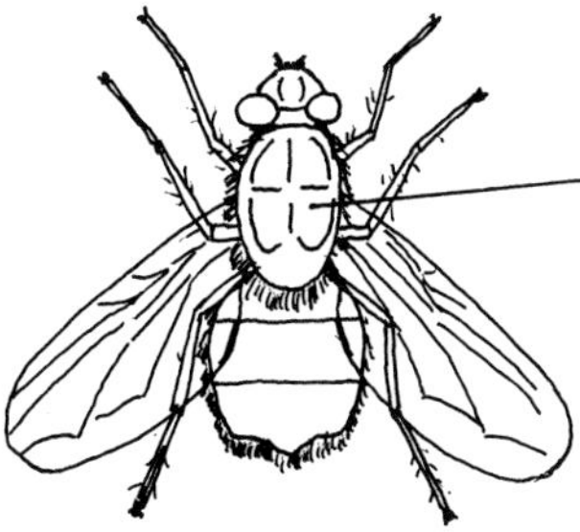

(Bluebottle)

TIN An element. A soft, silvery-white, malleable metal. It is used as tinfoil, and for coating steel to make 'tin' cans for food. Bronze is an alloy of tin and copper. Solder is an alloy of tin and lead.

The symbol for tin is Sn (from its old name stannum).

TISSUE A large number of similar cells (in an organism) grouped together.

TOP CARNIVORE The animal which is at the end of a food chain and which is not eaten by any other animal.

TRACHEA (pr. trak-ee-a) Another name for WINDPIPE.

TRANSECT LINE A string line placed across a habitat (e.g. a field) so that all the organisms touching the line can be counted or studied.

TRANSPIRATION The losing of water, in the form of water vapour, from the leaves of plants.

TRUTH TABLE A table showing the output values of a logic circuit for each of the input values (0 stands for low voltage; 1 stands for high voltage).
Example. The truth table for a NAND circuit with two inputs is

INPUTS		OUTPUT
0	0	1
0	1	1
1	0	1
1	1	0

TURBINE A device for converting the kinetic energy of a moving gas or liquid into other forms of energy by rotating (turning) blades.

Example. The turbines in a hydroelectric power station.

TWINS Two babies conceived (begun) at the same time.

Fraternal (non-identical) twins are formed when two eggs are fertilised at the same time. Fraternal twins can be both the same sex, or one of each sex, and do not normally look alike.

Identical twins are formed when a fertilised egg splits into two. They are always the same sex (either both boys or both girls) and look very much alike.

UMBILICAL CORD The tube which connects the embryo of a mammal with the placenta. When a human baby is born, the umbilical cord is cut and tied. The baby's end of the cord becomes its navel (or tummy-button).

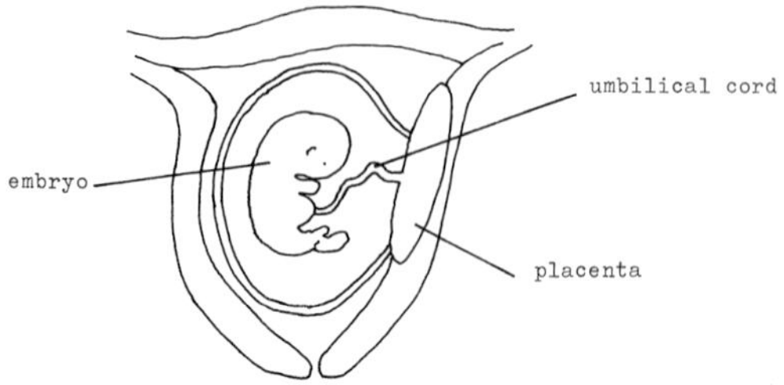

UNICELLULAR (pr. yoon-i-sell-yoo-ler) A unicellular organism is one which consists of only one cell. A single-celled organism.

Example. Amoeba.

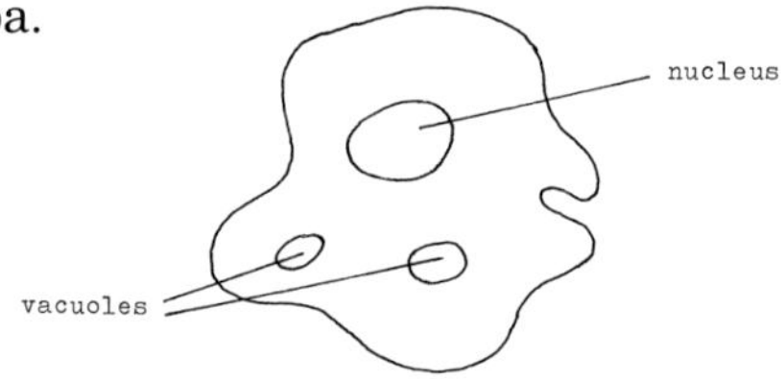

UNIVERSAL INDICATOR A mixture of dyes which will change colour according to the pH of the liquid to which it is added. The colours are approximately

pH 1 - 4	red	strong	
pH 5	orange	↕	ACID
pH 6	yellow	weak	
pH 7	green		NEUTRAL
pH 8	blue-green	weak	
pH 9	blue	↕	ALKALI
pH 10	blue-purple		
pH 11	purple	strong	

URETERS (pr. yoor-eet-uz) The two tubes through which urine passes from the kidneys to the bladder.

URETHRA (pr. yoor-eeth-ra) The tube through which urine (and, in males, semen) leaves the body. The opening of the urethra is at the end of the penis in a male, and in front of the vagina in a female.

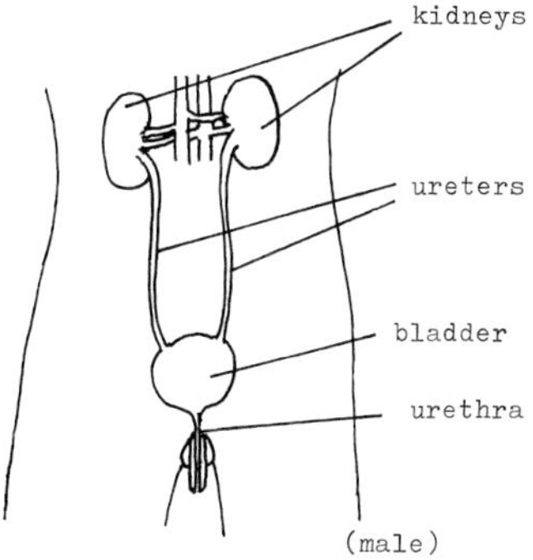

URINE (pr. yoor-in) The yellow liquid excretion produced by the kidneys. It contains water, urea, salts and other chemicals. It passes through the ureters to the bladder where it is stored before leaving the body through the urethra.

UTERUS (pr. yoo-ter-us) The part of a female mammal in which the embryo develops. Also called the womb (pr. woom).

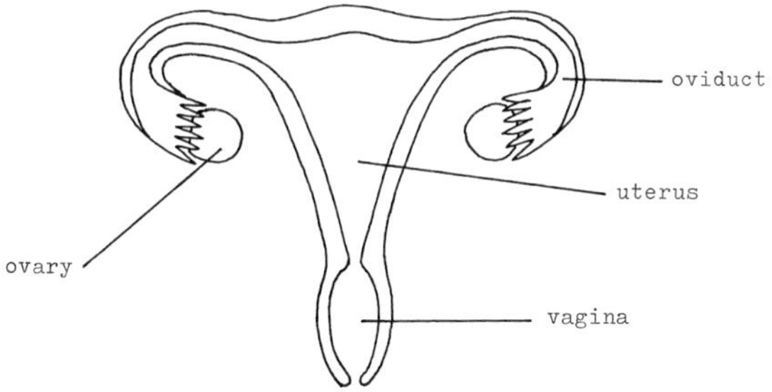

VACUOLE (pr. vak-yoo-ole) The watery part of a cell, containing cell sap (water, sugar and mineral salts), inside the cytoplasm, and separated from the cytoplasm by the inner cell membrane.

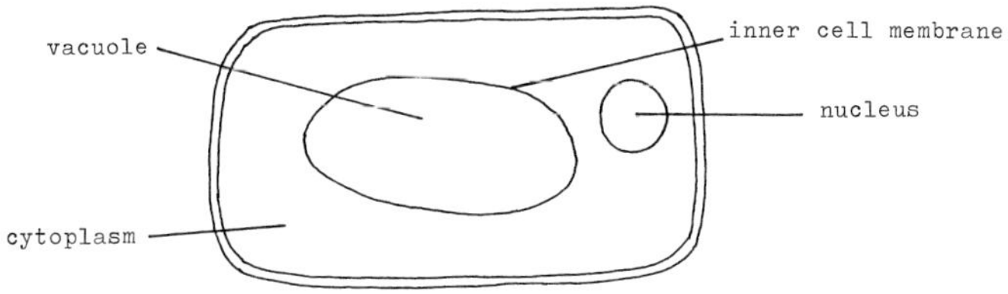

Large vacuoles develop inside fully-grown plant cells, but not normally in animal cells.

VACUUM (pr. vak-yoo-um) A space which contains nothing at all. No perfect vacuum exists, but some spaces are very nearly vacuums.
Example. Interstellar space (the space between the stars).

VAGINA (pr. ver-jy-na) The part of the female human (or other mammal) reproductive system below the uterus. When sexual intercourse takes place, the penis of the male is inserted into the vagina, and semen passes up the vagina to the uterus. During birth, the baby moves down the vagina from the uterus. The opening of the vagina is between the anus and the opening of the urethra. See UTERUS.

VAPOUR The gaseous state of a substance which is normally a liquid or a solid. The word 'vapour' is often used when the substance is a gas but is below its boiling point.

Example. Water vapour is produced when water evaporates. Normal air always contains some water vapour, as water evaporates very slowly even at ordinary temperatures. This is why puddles of water gradually dry up, and why ink from a pen dries on the paper.

VARIABLE RESISTOR A resistor whose resistance can be changed by varying the amount of resistant material through which the current flows.

Circuit diagram symbol 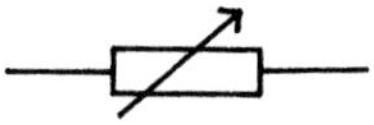

VEIN One of the large blood vessels (tubes) carrying blood to the heart.

VENTRAL At the front of an animal.
Example. The ventral scales of a snake are at the front of the snake.

VERTEBRATE An animal which has a backbone (spine, or spinal column).
Examples. Human being, frog.

VIBRATION Repeated movement backwards and forwards. Sound waves are caused by vibration.

VIRUS A tiny parasite which lives within the cell of another organism. A virus can exist on its own but it cannot grow or reproduce without its host organism.

Many viruses cause disease to humans (e.g. measles, mumps, common cold, flu, etc.), other animals and plants.

VISCOSITY The stickiness of a liquid.

Example. Treacle has a greater viscosity than water. It flows more slowly and is stickier.

VITAMIN One of a group of substances which the body needs in small amounts for maintaining good health.

Example. Vitamin C (or ascorbic acid) which is found in citrus fruits (such as oranges, lemons, etc.) and green vegetables.

VOLATILE A volatile substance is one which vaporises (turns into a vapour) easily.

VOLTAGE The force which is trying to push electrons through an electrical circuit. Also called electromotive force (EMF) and potential difference (PD).

The unit of voltage is the volt (V). Named after the Italian scientist Count Alessandro Volta (born 1745, died 1827).

Most equipment in houses works from a 240 volt supply, which can kill by electrocution. Model railways use a 12 volt supply, which is safe, and torches use 6 volts or less.

VOLTMETER An instrument which measures the voltage in a circuit. A voltmeter is always connected in parallel with the component across which the voltage is being measured.

Circuit diagram symbol 

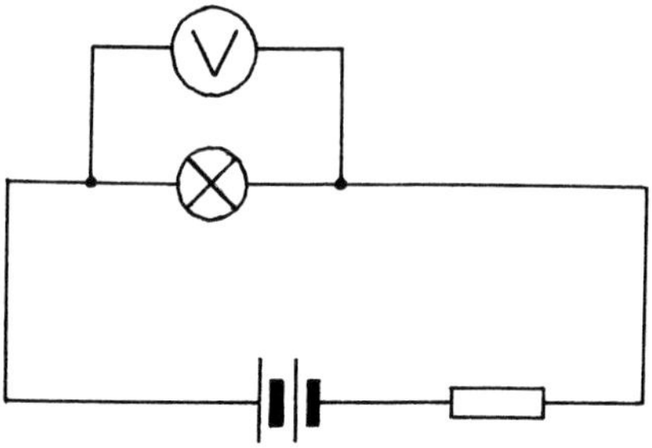

Voltmeter measuring the voltage across a lamp.

VOLUME (1) The amount of space occupied by an object or substance. Volume is usually measured in cubic centimetres (cm^3) or litres (l).

1000 cubic centimetres = 1000 millilitres = 1 litre
1000 cm^3 = 1000 ml = 1l
1 cm^3 = 1 c.c. = 1ml

(2) The loudness or intensity of a sound.

WARM-BLOODED With an almost constant (not changing) body temperature which is often higher than the outside temperature. Mammals and birds are warm-blooded animals (mammals about 37°C, birds about 39°C).

Warm-blooded animals are able to convert chemical energy (from food) into thermal (heat) energy and can therefore remain active in cold weather.

However, in very cold conditions they cannot manufacture thermal energy quickly enough, and may die of cold (hypothermia).

WATER A compound of hydrogen and oxygen. An oxide of hydrogen. Formula H_2O.

Pure water freezes at 0°C (to form ice) and boils at 100°C (to form steam). Its density is $1 g/cm^3$.

Water is the commonest liquid on the Earth. Apart from seas, lakes and rivers, there are large amounts of water under the ground. The air, even in dry places, contains water vapour. The human body is over 70% water and some fruit and vegetables are as much as 95% water.

Water is essential to all living things and is used by man in many ways, e.g. as a solvent, as a source of power (hydroelectric power), etc.

WATER OF CRYSTALLISATION Water which combines with a chemical to form crystals of the chemical.

Example. The water in blue copper sulphate.

A salt which contains water of crystallisation is a hydrated salt.

WATT A unit of power. Named after the Scottish engineer James Watt (born 1736, died 1819).

Electrical power can be calculated by multiplying the current by the voltage.

Watts = amps x volts.

Example. An electric fire with a power of 750 watts operating from a 250 volt supply uses 3 amps of current because 750 = 3 x 250.

1000 watts = 1 kilowatt.

WAVELENGTH The distance between similar points on two adjacent (next door) cycles of a wave.

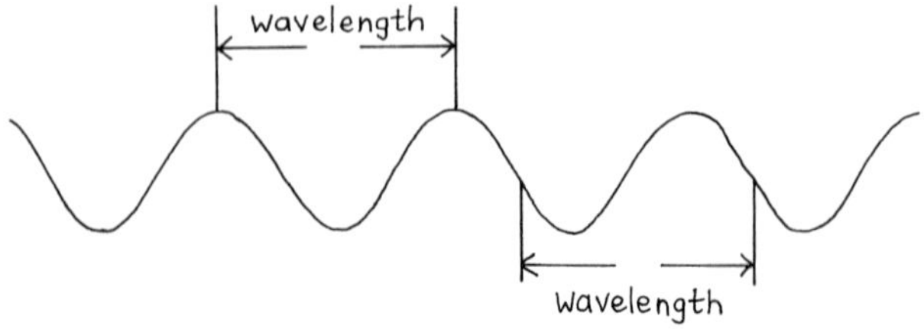

WEIGHT The force with which a mass is attracted by gravity. On the Earth, the force acting on a mass of 1 kilogram is about 10 newtons. See MASS.

WINDPIPE The air passage connecting the throat to the lungs. Also called trachea. See LUNGS.

WOMB (pr. woom) Another name for uterus. See UTERUS.

WORD-EQUATION An equation made up of chemical names to show a chemical reaction.

Example. zinc + oxygen = zinc oxide.

WORK The transfer of energy when a force moves, calculated by multiplying the force by the distance through which it moves. Usually measured in joules.

Joules = newtons x metres

YEAST One of a group of fungi which, during anaerobic respiration, ferment sugar to make alcohol and carbon dioxide, e.g. in beer and wine making. In bread making, the bubbles of carbon dioxide make the bread rise.

ZINC An element. A white brittle metal. Used for making brass (an alloy of copper and zinc) and for galvanising (coating) iron to prevent corrosion.

The symbol for zinc is Zn.

ZYGOTE The cell formed by the joining together of a male gamete and a female gamete during fertilisation. It develops into an embryo.